W9-CSE-859

IONIC CRYSTALS, LATTICE DEFECTS AND NONSTOICHIOMETRY

IONIC CRYSTALS LATTICE DEFECTS AND NONSTOICHIOMETRY

N. N. GREENWOOD

Professor of Inorganic Chemistry
University of Newcastle upon Tyne

CHEMICAL PUBLISHING COMPANY INC.
NEW YORK 1970

CHEM

FIRST AMERICAN EDITION
1970

CHEMICAL PUBLISHING CO. INC.
NEW YORK, N.Y.

First published in 1968

Suggested U.D.C. number: 54-16: 548·71

Printed photolitho in Great Britain by Page Bros. (Norwich) Ltd., Mile Cross Lane,
Norwich

PREFACE

THERE comes a time in the development of each branch of science when the underlying principles gradually become clear to those working in that area. At such a juncture the availability of an appropriate monograph or textbook becomes particularly desirable and its lack tends to impede further progress. Solid state physics has passed through this stage during the last decade and has been well served by many definitive books at several levels. The closely related chemical aspects of the defect solid state have not been so fortunate and, partly for this reason, this important area of chemistry has not received adequate attention in undergraduate and graduate courses. Indeed, unlike the molecular orbital treatment of covalent compounds and the ligand field theory of transition element complexes, both of which have recently been well treated in numerous books at various levels of sophistication, the bonding theory of the defect solid state has been sadly neglected in student textbooks and monographs. The present book was written to remedy this situation and is based on lectures which the author has given at various times during the last 15 years.

The elementary aspects of bonding in predominantly ionic solids have been treated in innumerable books, but frequently the treatment has been based on a physical formalism which oversimplifies the chemical realities and which fails to recognize that chemistry is not merely an exercise in solid geometry and elementary electrostatics. A discussion of simple ionic solids is included in the opening chapters partly to rectify this lack of chemical interpretation which characterizes so many existing treatments of the subject and partly to introduce systematically the concepts required in the later treatment of the defect solid state.

The treatment is then broadened to include the thermodynamic aspects of regular crystalline arrays of ions and again the chemical implications and consequences are stressed. The theoretical sections are supplemented by brief accounts of the experimental techniques available for studying the phenomena discussed. The extension to nonstoichiometric solids follows naturally and the present state of knowledge of these intriguing systems is reviewed. The chemical implications and technological importance of these defect solid structures are briefly mentioned but the treatment concentrates on principles rather than applications. Thus the book aims at

v

providing for the first time a systematic and integrated account of modern ideas on the role of lattice defects in modifying the properties of ionic solids, coupled with a didactic treatment of the problems posed by the occurrence of compounds of variable composition and the apparent existence of grossly nonstoichiometric phases.

The final draft of the manuscript was prepared during the tenure of a visiting professorship at Michigan State University, East Lansing, and financed by the U.S. National Science Foundation. It is a pleasure to acknowledge the hospitality, friendship and help extended to me by Professor A. I. Popov, Professor A. Timnick, and other members of the academic and secretarial staff of the Chemistry Department at M.S.U. I am also most grateful to Professor E. E. Aynsley and my other colleagues in Newcastle upon Tyne for so willingly undertaking extra commitments during my absence, and to Dr. I. J. McColm for reading the manuscript and making many helpful comments. I would also like to thank Miss Karen Greenwood and Mr. Arthur Howe for their great help in reading proofs. Finally, I would like to record how much this book owes to the personal influence of Professor J. S. Anderson who first introduced me to this fascinating area of chemistry as a graduate student in the University of Melbourne many years ago and whose continuing contributions to the development of this subject will be clear to all who read these pages.

N. N. GREENWOOD

CONTENTS

vii

CONTENTS

THE SOLID STATE: IONIC CRYSTALS

1.1. Historical Introduction

THE regularity of crystal shapes has excited attention from earliest times and peoples' imagination has been stirred by the elegant symmetry of natural crystals and by their glorious colours. Indeed many gemstones were thought to possess magical properties and even today they are frequently prized for their sentimental value as much as for their rarity. The scientific investigation of crystals dates from 1669 when Nicolaus Steno discovered the law of constant interfacial angles for the special case of rock salt (sodium chloride). Since that time our understanding of the properties of crystalline solids has passed through four main stages of development:

(i) the study of bulk properties of crystals, especially their external shape (1669–1840) ;

(ii) the description of crystal symmetries in terms of point lattices (1842–1912);

(iii) the use of X-ray diffraction to determine crystal structures and the development of a bonding theory for ideal ionic crystals (1912–1926, and later refinements to the present day);

(iv) the recognition of lattice defects and their influence on the properties of real crystals (1926 onwards).

The first stage involved a study of the macroscopic or bulk properties of crystals. In the same year that the law of constant interfacial angles was discovered (1669) the double refraction of crystals was first noticed by Erasmus Bartolinus in Iceland spar (calcium carbonate) and shortly thereafter (1690) Huygens discovered the phenomenon of plane polarization of light in the rays transmitted by that crystal. During the following century the methods of optical crystallography were developed and in 1784 Haüy, drawing on earlier work by Romé de l'Isle (1772), suggested that the different forms which a given crystalline substance adopts are all based on a common underlying structure. This led to his formulation of the law of rational intercepts, that the form of crystals could be uniquely described by reference to crystal axes, their relative lengths and angles of inclination. The axes so defined marked out a unit cell which was the smallest unit to possess the symmetry of the crystal as a whole. The law is now usually expressed in terms of Miller indices introduced in 1839 and led ultimately to the recognition of the seven systems of crystal symmetry: cubic, hexagonal, tetragonal, orthorhombic, rhombohedral, monoclinic, and triclinic. The culmination of this first stage of the development of the macroscopic properties of crystals was the complete description of the various symmetries of these cells by reference to the thirty-two point groups or classes of crystal symmetry (Hessel, 1830).

The second stage of development involved a description of the lattice properties of crystals. Frankenheim in 1842 showed that there were 15 symmetrical ways of arranging networks of points in space, and Bravais in 1848 showed that two of these were identical. The fourteen space lattices which are illustrated in *Figure 1.1* were divided amongst the seven systems of crystal symmetry as shown in *Table 1.1*:

Table 1.1
Classification of space lattices

Symmetry system	Space lattice
cubic	simple cube; body-centred cube; face-centred cube
hexagonal	hexagonal prism
tetragonal	tetragonal prism; body-centred tetragonal prism
orthorhombic	rectangular prism; body-centred rectangular prism; base-centred rectangular prism; face-centred rectangular prism
rhombohedral	rhombohedron
monoclinic	monoclinic parallelopiped; monoclinic base-centred parallelopiped
triclinic	triclinic parallelopiped

From these seven fundamental lattices Sohncke (1879) generated 65 lattices by performing the three operations (*i*) translation, i.e. moving the lattice parallel to itself, (*ii*) rotation of the lattice about an axis, and (*iii*) screw motion, a combination of translation and rotation about a screw axis. Independent contributions by Schoenflies (1888), Federov (1890) and Barlow (1894) added a fourth operation (*iv*) reflection which, in combination with translation and rotation, led to reflection and glide planes of symmetry, to axes of rotatory inversion, and to centres of inversion. These so-called elements of symmetry of the second kind relate right-handed to left-handed systems and together with the earlier operations

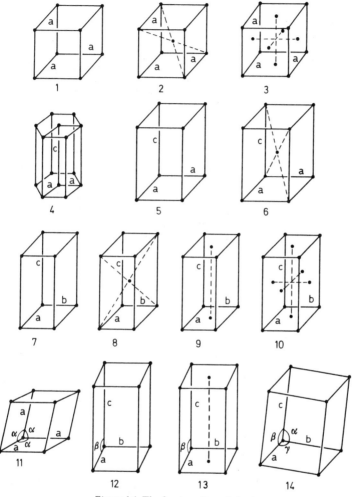

Figure 1.1. The fourteen Bravais lattices

(1) simple cube, (2) body-centred cube, (3) face-centred cube, (4) hexagonal prism, (5) simple tetragonal prism, (6) body-centred tetragonal prism, (7) rectangular (orthorhombic) prism, (8) body-centred rectangular prism, (9) base-centred rectangular prism, (10) face-centred rectangular prism, (11) rhombohedron, (12) simple monoclinic parallelopiped, (13) base-centred monoclinic parallelopiped, (14) triclinic parallelopiped

lead ultimately to the 230 space groups. It is not possible to conceive of any further geometrical groups which can repeat themselves infinitely in three dimensions. The culmination of this second stage of development was von Laue's suggestion in 1912 that in real crystals these hypothetical lattice points would be occupied by atoms and so could act as a three-dimensional diffraction grating for electromagnetic radiation of appropriate wavelength (X-rays).

The third stage in the development of our understanding of the properties of crystalline solids was inaugurated by the experimental substantiation of von Laue's ideas by Friedrich and Knipping in 1912 using zinc sulphide as the crystal. Shortly thereafter W. L. Bragg simplified the interpretation by considering the reflection of X-rays from the crystal planes and correctly deduced the structures of the first two crystals to be solved by X-ray techniques, those of sodium chloride and potassium chloride (1912). Results on diamond (1913), ZnS, FeS_2, CaF_2 and $CaCO_3$ (1914) followed rapidly to be succeeded by many more—the science of X-ray crystallography had been launched. Other early developments were the theory of Fourier analysis (W. H. Bragg, 1915) and the powder photographic method (Debye and Scherrer, 1916; Hull, 1917). With the establishment of the presence of regular arrays of atoms and ions in crystals the way was open for the development of a theory of ionic crystals. Early work by Born and Landé (1918) was followed by calculations of the Madelung constant for most of the simple, highly symmetrical structures by Madelung (1918) and Ewald (1921). The Born–Haber cycle also dates from this time (1919) and it became clear that the binding energy of simple ionic lattices could be understood quite readily. This theory of the lattice energy of ideal crystals together with Goldschmidt's ideas on ionic radii and their influence on crystal structure (1926) are developed in the opening chapters of this book.

The fourth and final stage in the development of theories of ionic crystals concerns the recognition that many physical and chemical properties of real crystals can only be interpreted in terms of imperfections. The concept of lattice defects and their interactions was introduced by Frenkel (1926), Wagner and Schottky (1930) and Jost (1933) and will be treated in detail in later chapters of this book. The recognition of such defects has had a profound influence on our understanding of such diverse phenomena as solid-state reactions, heterogeneous catalysis, the strength of materials, the properties of semiconductors and transistors, the colour of crystals and the existence of nonstoichiometric phases of variable composition. The field is still being actively developed but an attempt will be made to

4

give a broad presentation of ideas which have gained general acceptance.

1.2. The Concept of Nonstoichiometry

Although it is now over 35 years since ideas on lattice defects and nonstoichiometry began to evolve systematically, it is surprising how little the results have impinged on presentations of chemical theory, particularly at the more elementary levels. Here progress is still blocked by a slavish devotion to the cult of the molecule and a naïve faith in the general applicability of Dalton's laws of chemical combination. It is perhaps instructive to see how this situation arose and how readily it can be remedied.

The concept of the molecule arose initially from a study of the gaseous state which had earlier led directly to Dalton's atomic theory. Because the systems being studied were gas-phase inorganic reactions, the laws of constant composition and simple proportion followed inevitably. However, it should not be forgotten that in the early part of the last century there was a bitter controversy between Proust and Berthollet, and the latter brought much cogent evidence to support his contention that, for *solid* compounds, constancy of composition was by no means universal and variation in composition frequently occurred. His data were not refuted but gradually became ignored due to the upsurge of interest in the new organic chemistry. This tended to warp the balanced development of chemical theory, since two of the main characteristics of organic compounds are (*a*) they are molecular, and (*b*) carbon has a constant valency of four. The dramatic success of valency theory in the hands of people like Frankland, Kekulé, and Thiele tended to obscure the fact that many (inorganic) compounds could not be satisfactorily described in these terms. An indication of how the constant quadrivalency of carbon led to the basic structural elements of organic molecules can be gained by considering the formulae of a few simple hydrocarbons:

CH_4, C_2H_6, C_3H_8—concept of chains (rather than valencies of 4, 3, 2·67 for carbon);

C_2H_6, C_2H_4, C_2H_2—concept of single, double, and triple bonds;

C_3H_6, C_5H_6, C_6H_6—concept of rings, unsaturated rings and aromaticity.

That this development was a matter of pragmatism rather than logic, can be seen from the fact that the simple theory is completely inadequate to interpret the structure and stoichiometry of the boranes: B_2H_6, B_4H_8, B_5H_9, B_5H_{11}, etc.

5

Now that adequate theories of inorganic chemistry have been devised, it is recognized that variability of valency is far more common amongst the elements than is constancy. What is perhaps less familiar is that, if a compound consists not of molecules but of an infinite array of ions, then valency and composition can often vary continuously. For example ferrous oxide does not have the composition FeO; such a composition is unstable under all conditions of temperature and pressure. The phase varies in composition between about $Fe_{0.94}O$ and $Fe_{0.86}O$ by leaving some Fe^{2+} sites vacant and raising the charge on twice this number of the remaining cations from Fe^{2+} to Fe^{3+}. Such behaviour clearly requires revision of the classical ideas of 'valency', 'compound' and the simple laws of chemical combination. It should be emphasized that, at the atomic level, the changes in oxidation state of an individual ion are integral but that, because of the effectively infinite array of ions, variations in the overall stoichiometry of the phase appear continuous.

A second type of composition change can arise by substitution of one element by another. Isomorphous substitution was recognized by Mitscherlich (1819), but it occurs much more widely than this. The maintenance of a particular structure is often dependent more on the relative size of an ion (in Å) than on its charge. For example, in the mineral silicates,

Na^+ (0·95 Å) can substitute for Ca^{2+} (0·99 Å);
Li^+ (0·60 Å) can substitute for Mg^{2+} (0·65) but not for Na^+ (0·95);
Mg^{2+} (0·65 Å) can substitute for Fe^{2+} (0·76) or Fe^{3+} (0·64) but not for Ca^{2+} (0·99).

Where there is a change in ionic charge, there must be a corresponding compensation elsewhere in the crystal. For example, $(Fe^{3+} + Na^+)$ can replace $(Mg^{2+} + Ca^{2+})$ and $(Ba^{2+} + Al^{3+})$ can replace $(K^+ + Si^{4+})$, etc.

1.3. Evidence for the Existence of Ions in Solids

Cogent evidence for the existence of ions in crystalline solids comes from a variety of sources though much pseudo-evidence on this point has also been offered in the past. It cannot be too frequently stressed that melting point and solubility are unreliable indicators of bond type in solids and even electrical conductivity can be misleading. Thus, a substance is not necessarily ionic because it has a high melting point; diamond, which is covalent, has an extremely high melting point and so does tungsten, which is a metal. Many similar examples could be given. Likewise, solubility in a solvent of high dielectric constant is an unreliable criterion for ionic bonding since sugar (covalent) is very soluble in water whereas barium sulphate (ionic) is not. Compounds which give conducting solutions may have reacted with the solvent; for example, the covalent, molecular solid phosphorus pentoxide gives a highly conducting aqueous solution. Even the ionic conductivity of fused compounds does not necessarily reflect the type of bonding in the solid state since the phase change can also involve a change in bond type. Numerous examples are now known of which the following are typical: solid ionic aluminium chloride Al^{3+} $(Cl^-)_3$ melts to give a covalent, molecular non-conducting liquid Al_2Cl_6; conversely, solid, covalent boron trifluoride dihydrate, $BF_3 \cdot 2H_2O$, melts below room temperature to give a completely ionized liquid $(H_3O^+)(F_3BOH^-)$. The ionic conductivity of crystalline solids themselves at high temperatures is considered in Chapter 4.

X-ray diffraction techniques normally give only the positions of the component species and not their charges. More sophisticated analysis is required to establish the presence of ions. A very precise count of electron density in the Fourier contour map of, say, sodium chloride shows that each sodium nucleus is surrounded by 10 electrons (Na^+) and each chlorine nucleus by 18 electrons (Cl^-). Furthermore, the X-ray powder patterns of NaCl and KCl are different despite the fact that both have the NaCl-type structure; this is because the scattering power, f, of an atom or ion (which depends on the number of electrons) influences the intensity, F, of the lines. For the NaCl-type structure

$$F \text{ (all Miller indices even)} = f_{metal} + f_{halogen}$$

$$F \text{ (all Miller indices odd)} = f_{metal} - f_{halogen}$$

Reflections with odd Miller indices h,k,l are therefore present for NaCl but missing from KCl since both K^+ and Cl^- have 18 electrons. Considerable experimental precision is required before these lines of evidence become convincing.

A more general argument for the presence of ions comes from the absence of other plausible types of bonding. For example, lithium chloride is observed not to have metallic properties such as high electronic conductivity, and there are insufficient electrons on each lithium atom to permit the formation of covalent electron-pair bonds to the six surrounding chlorine atoms. The only alternative to ionic bonding therefore would be an assembly of atoms—but these would be paramagnetic or antiferromagnetic as lithium and chlorine atoms each have an odd number of electrons. However, the crystal is known to behave as a normal diamagnetic compound, consistent with the presence of the spin-paired ions Li^+ and Cl^-. Neutron diffraction studies would also detect unpaired electrons because the neutron itself has a magnetic moment. The magnetic properties of many crystalline compounds of transition elements and lanthanide elements reveal the number of unpaired electrons on the lattice units: these are consistent with the presence of ions rather than atoms or covalently bonded species. Electron spin resonance measurements, especially on elements with unpaired f electrons, also show how closely the ions in crystal matrices follow the behaviour of free gas-phase ions. The optical absorption spectra of gas-phase ions are quite characteristic of each species and the appearance of the same spectra in crystals again argues for the presence of those same ions in the condensed phase. More recently Mössbauer spectroscopy (nuclear γ-ray resonance fluorescence) has afforded abundant evidence for the existence of ions both in crystalline compounds and as dilute solutions in solid matrices, though the detailed arguments are too long to repeat here.[1]

Finally, cogent evidence for the presence of ions in alkali halide crystals and related compounds comes from the direct calculation of their heats of formation. Even the simplest calculations based on an ionic model give excellent agreement with experimental values. Such calculations form the subject of the next chapter.

Bibliography

1. Bragg, W. L., The Crystalline State, Bell, London, 1949
2. Evans, R. C., An Introduction to Crystal Chemistry (2nd edn), Cambridge University Press, 1964
3. Partington, J. R., An Advanced Treatise on Physical Chemistry Vol. III, The Properties of Solids, Longmans, Green, London, 1952
4. Monteath Robertson, J., Chapt 2 in Mandelcorn, L. (Ed.) Non-stoichiometry, Academic Press, New York, 1964
5. Bijvoet, J. M., Kolkmeyer, N. H. and MacGillavry, C. H., X-ray Analysis of Crystals, Butterworths, London, 1951
6. Rees, A. L. G., Chemistry of the Defect Solid State, Methuen, London, 1954

[1] Wertheim, G. K., Mössbauer Effect: Principles and Applications, Academic Paperbacks, New York, 1964

2

LATTICE ENERGY OF IONIC CRYSTALS

THERE are two basic aspects of the theory of ionic bonding:
(a) the energetics of ionic bond formation and the calculation of lattice energies;
(b) the geometrical aspects of crystal shape and symmetry and the distortion effects of polarization.

The first of these topics is discussed in the present chapter and the geometrical properties of ionic crystals is considered in Chapter 3.

Before dealing with the general question of lattice energies it is instructive to consider the various factors which determine whether a given pair of atoms in the gas phase will unite to form an isolated ion pair. The process of forming this ionic bond can be broken up into four distinct stages which will be considered in turn:

(i) production of an isolated positive ion;
(ii) production of an isolated negative ion;
(iii) coulombic attraction of the ions so-formed;
(iv) close-range repulsion of the ions.

The standard of reference for the potential energy of the system will be the energy of the separated atom, taken as zero. The unit of energy used throughout is the kilocalorie: 1 kcal = 4·1833 kJ.

2.1. Production of an Isolated Cation

The energy required to remove an electron from an alkali metal atom is the ionization potential, I_M:

$$M \rightarrow M^+ + e^- ; \qquad \Delta H = I_M$$

For a Group II metal the sum of the first two ionization potentials is required and for a Group III element the sum of the first three ionization potentials. Values of these quantities are listed in *Table 2.1* and a complete list of the successive ionization potentials of the elements is given in the Appendix.

Three trends are immediately apparent from *Table 2.1*: firstly, the ionization potential decreases steadily with increase in atomic number within each main group of inert-gas core ions; secondly, the energy required for ionization increases rapidly with increase in ionic charge; and thirdly, the energy required to ionize atoms with a d^{10} core of electrons is invariably greater than for the corresponding ion with an inert-gas core. These trends can readily be understood in terms of the size of the ion and its effective nuclear charge.

Table 2.1
Ionization energies (in kcal/g atom)

$M \rightarrow M^+ + e^-$		$M \rightarrow M^{2+} + 2e^-$		$M \rightarrow M^{3+} + 3e^-$	
inert gas core	d^{10} *ion core*	*inert gas core*	d^{10} *ion core*	*inert gas core*	d^{10} *ion core*
Li 124·32		Be 634·9		B 1646·0	
Na 118·50		Mg 523·0		Al 1228·1	
K 100·08	Cu 178·15	Ca 424·4	Zn 630·6	Sc 1016·9	Ga 1319·5
Rb 96·32	Ag 174·7	Sr 385·6	Cd 597·3	Y 902·3	In 1214·9
Cs 89·79	Au 212·7	Ba 350·8	Hg 673·0	La 835·2	Tl 1299·1

Within any one group, the size of an element increases with increase in atomic number and this diminishes the coulomb attraction between the ionic core and the electron being removed. This is partly offset by the increase in positive nuclear charge for the heavier elements, but this extra charge is almost completely shielded for the main group elements in *Table 2.1*. The trend to greater electropositivity is not entirely general, however, as can be illustrated by the ionization potentials and chemical properties of the heavier transition metals; these are all 'more noble' than the first row transition elements because the lanthanide contraction severely reduces the normal influence of increased size in lowering the ionization potentials. The effect is apparent for gold, mercury, and even thallium in *Table 2.1*. Likewise, the d^{10} ions are all smaller than their inert-gas core precursors and this increases the energy required to remove the electrons; this is reinforced by the incomplete shielding of the ten added units of positive charge on the nuclei by the ten added electrons. The rapid increase in total ionization energy for the multicharged ions also stems from the progressively decreasing size of the ions and the progressively increasing charge against which the successive electrons must be removed.

The ease of forming an ionic bond clearly correlates with the ease of forming the cationic component of the gaseous ion pair. In view of the tremendous energies required to ionize beryllium and boron it is not surprising that these elements do not form simple ionic compounds. The most likely elements to form ionic bonds are the alkali metals, followed by the alkaline earth metals and the heavier elements in Group III. In other cases coordination or solvation can sometimes stabilize ion formation by releasing some of the energy required in the form of ion-dipole coulomb attractions or specific ion-ligand bond formation, e.g. $[Al(H_2O)_6]^{3+}$.

2.2. Production of an Isolated Anion

The second stage in the process of forming an isolated ion pair is the production of an anion from the non-metal atom:

$$X + e^- \rightarrow X^-; \qquad \Delta H = -E_X$$

Precise numerical values are much more difficult to obtain than for ionization potentials and different methods sometimes give values differing by several kcal/g atom. Some typical values for electron affinities, E_X, are given in *Table 2.2* which shows that this process

Table 2.2
Electron affinities of non-metal atoms[1]

Product ion	E_X kcal/g atom	Product ion	E_X kcal/g atom	Product ion	E_X kcal/g atom
F⁻	79·5 ± 2	O⁻	33·8 ± 10	O²⁻	−172 ± 5
Cl⁻	85·5 ± 1·5	S⁻	49·6 ± 3	S²⁻	−100 ± 2
Br⁻	80·5 ± 1	Se⁻	50·7 ± 3	Se²⁻	−117 ± 2
I⁻	73·6 ± 1	Te⁻	53 ± ?	Te²⁻	−97 ± ?
At⁻	61 ± ?				

[1] Selected from Ladd, M. F. C. and Lee, W. H., *Prog. Solid St. Chem.*, 1 (1963) 37; 2 (1965) 378 and references therein.

evolves energy for the halogens and also for the first electron added to oxygen and the chalcogens. In these cases it is conventional (though confusing) to call E_X positive. To understand why energy should be released when an electron is added to certain neutral atoms we must consider three effects which determine the energy change:

(*i*) the coulomb attraction of the nucleus for the added electron;
(*ii*) the coulomb repulsion of the orbital electrons for the added electron;
(*iii*) the energy associated with (*a*) orbital angular momentum and (*b*) spin angular momentum of the electrons.

At large distances the coulomb forces (*i*) and (*ii*) cancel and the third term is unmodified so there is little interaction. However, at closer range, when the added electron occupies one of the atomic orbitals, the nucleus is not so effectively screened and there may be a net

11

attraction. This is particularly so if the electron is being added to a partly filled s orbital since the screening of one s electron by another in the same orbital is rather ineffective; in this connexion it is relevant that hydrogen and the alkali metals (like the halogens) all evolve energy when an electron is added, e.g. $Na(3s^1) \rightarrow Na^-(3s^2)$, $E_X = 28$ kcal/mole. This energy is considerably in excess of the spin coupling energy $(iii)(b)$ and, of course, the orbital angular momentum $(iii)(a)$ of an s electron is zero by definition. When p electrons are involved the orbital angular momentum term $(iii)(a)$ must also be considered and this is probably the dominant effect in producing positive electron affinities for the halogens and Group VI elements; the full effect will be reduced slightly because p orbitals so not penetrate as close to the nucleus as do s orbitals and hence inter-electronic repulsions (ii) tend to outweigh the attraction (i) of the well-shielded nucleus for the added electron. The extent of this net repulsion arising from the coulomb components of the electron affinity for a p electron can be gauged from the special case of nitrogen, for which the electron affinity is actually negative $(E_X = -16)$: in the nitrogen atom there is virtually no orbital angular momentum coupling energy $(iii)(a)$ since the electron configuration of the atom $(2p_x{}^1, 2p_y{}^1, 2p_z{}^1)$ results in an S spectroscopic ground state with zero resultant orbital angular momentum. The negative electron affinity therefore reflects the excess of the electron–electron coulomb repulsion (ii) over the electron–nuclear coulomb attraction (i). Again the spin angular momentum coupling energy $(iii)(b)$ is very small. In summary:

for an added s electron, term (i) predominates over term (ii) and term (iii) can be neglected;

for an added p electron, term $(iii)(a)$ predominates but is reduced somewhat by the slight excess of term (ii) over term (i). An idea of the magnitude of this slight excess can be gauged from nitrogen where term $(iii)(a)$ is abnormally low for a p electron.

When more than one electron is added to form an ion the process is always endothermic because the second and subsequent electrons must be added against the coulomb repulsive interaction of the existing negative charge on the ion.

Thus	$O + e^- \rightarrow O^-$;	$-\Delta H = 34$ kcal/mole
	$O^- + e^- \rightarrow O^{2-}$;	$-\Delta H = -206$ kcal/mole
Hence	$O + 2e^- \rightarrow O^{2-}$;	$E_X(O^{2-}) = -172$ kcal/mole
Likewise	$N + 3e^- \rightarrow N^{3-}$;	$E_X(N^{3-}) = -511$ kcal/mole

12

Two further important points emerge from *Table 2.2* and its comparison with *Table 2.1*. The first is that, with the exception of the halogens, it is wrong to say (as the early 'octet theory' did) that atoms *want* to attain an inert-gas configuration. It always requires energy to ionize metal atoms and to place more than one electron on a non-metal atom. Secondly, *Tables 2.1* and *2.2* indicate that for no pair of atoms is the energy which can be recovered from the electron affinity greater than the ionization potential. In other words, for any pair of atoms in the Periodic Table it always requires energy to remove an electron from the metal atom and place it on the non-metal and the energy of $(M^+ + X^-)$ infinitely separated in the gas phase is always higher than the energy of $(M + X)$ in the gas phase. The most favourable combination is caesium and chlorine for which $I_M - E_X = 4.2$ kcal. If an ionic bond is to be formed, leading to a stable ion pair, some further interaction energy is required and this is discussed in the next section.

2.3. Coulombic Attraction of Ions

The attractive force, F, between a cation of charge $+z_1e$ and an anion of charge $-z_2e$ separated by a distance r is

$$F = z_1 z_2 e^2 / r^2 \tag{1}$$

The coulombic potential energy, Φ_c, is then given by the integral

$$\Phi_c = \int_\infty^r (z_1 z_2 e^2 / r^2)\, dr \tag{2}$$

whence

$$\Phi_c = -z_1 z_2 e^2 / r \tag{3}$$

The closer the two ions approach, the greater the attractive force and the lower the potential energy of the system. As seen in *Figure 2.1* there is a point $r = R$ when the hyperbola crosses the abscissa and at this separation it requires zero energy to transfer the electron from the metal to the non-metal. It is a simple matter to calculate what this distance is for univalent ions and the typical case of sodium and chlorine is considered below. The energy ΔH, required to remove an electron from a sodium atom and place it on a chlorine atom held at a distance r is

$$\Delta H = I_M - E_X - e^2 / r \tag{4}$$

When $r = R$ this energy is zero so

$$I_M - E_X - e^2 / R = 0$$

13

whence

$$R = \frac{e^2}{I_M - E_X} \qquad (5)$$

Substituting for I_M and E_X from *Tables 2.1* and *2.2* and remembering that $e = 4 \cdot 803 \times 10^{-10}$ e.s.u., $N = 6 \cdot 023 \times 10^{23}$, 1 kcal $= 4 \cdot 184 \times 10^{10}$ erg, and 1 Å $= 10^{-8}$ cm, we find

$$R = 10 \cdot 0\,\text{Å}$$

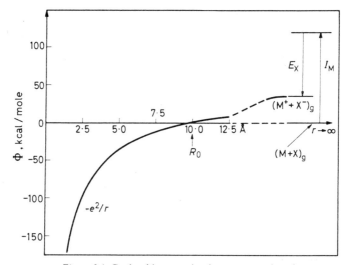

Figure 2.1. Coulombic attraction between gas-phase ions

It is clear that the lower I_M or the greater E_X, the more readily will M and X be linked electrovalently. But the model is not yet complete because, as it stands, the lowest energy of the system will be at $r = 0$ when the two ions have coalesced. To prevent this we need the intervention of a repulsive force which operates when the ions approach close together. The nature of this force will be considered in the following section.

2.4. Close-range Repulsion of Ions

When electrons are confined to a small region of space, their momentum and hence their energy increases, as a manifestation of the Heisenberg uncertainty principle. When two ions are in contact,

14

therefore, an effective repulsive force operates which resists closer approach. The force is quantum-mechanical in nature and operates in addition to any net mutual coulombic repulsion which the outer electron shells of the two ions have for each other. It is clearly a short-range interaction which increases very rapidly with decrease in internuclear separation. Born originally suggested a repulsive term, Φ_r, of the form b/r^n where b is a constant and the integer n depends on the nature of the ion and is normally in the range 5–12. In view of the known exponential dependence of the radial functions of atomic orbitals this term was later replaced by an analogous two-parameter expression

$$\Phi_r = b\,e^{-r/\rho} \tag{6}$$

The total potential energy of the two ions is then $\Phi = \Phi_c + \Phi_r$:

$$\Phi = -\frac{z_1 z_2 e^2}{r} + b\,e^{-r/\rho} \tag{7}$$

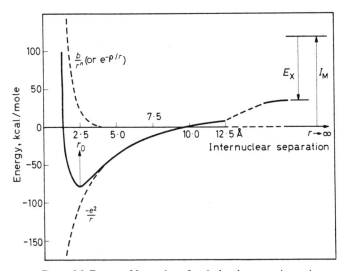

Figure 2.2. Energy of formation of an isolated gaseous ion-pair

This is illustrated in Figure 2.2. At the equilibrium separation, r_0, we have $(\partial\Phi/\partial r) = 0$, i.e.

$$\frac{z_1 z_2 e^2}{r_0^{\,2}} - \frac{b}{\rho}e^{-r_0/\rho} = 0 \tag{8}$$

whence

$$b = \frac{\rho}{r_0} \cdot \frac{z_1 z_2 e^2}{r_0} e^{r_0/\rho} \tag{9}$$

Substitution in (7) gives the minimum of potential energy as

$$\Phi_0 = -\frac{z_1 z_2 e^2}{r_0} \left(1 - \frac{\rho}{r_0}\right) \tag{10}$$

For many ions with inert gas configurations ρ is approximately 0·35 Å and typical values for r_0 are 2·0–4·0 Å; hence the repulsive term accounts for some 10–20 per cent of the final ionic interaction energy. The term becomes smaller the larger the ions, as would be expected from the nature of its origin.

As an example of the use of these formula, let us calculate the energy evolved when one sodium atom and one chlorine atom ionize and form an ion-pair with the observed internuclear separation in the gas phase [$r_0 = 2·51$ Å (note this is somewhat smaller than the internuclear distance in crystalline sodium chloride, viz. 2·814 Å)]:

$$\Delta H = I_M - E_X - \frac{e^2}{r_0}\left(1 - \frac{\rho}{r_0}\right) \tag{11}$$

$$= 118·5 - 85·5 - \frac{(4·80 \times 10^{-10})^2 \times 6·02 \times 10^{23}}{2·51 \times 10^{-8} \times 4·18 \times 10^{10}}$$

$$\times \left(1 - \frac{0·35}{2·51}\right)\text{kcal/mole}$$

$$= 33·0 - 132\,(1 - 0·139)\ \text{kcal/mole}$$

$$= -80\ \text{kcal/mole}$$

The formation of gaseous Na^+Cl^- is thus attended by considerable evolution of heat and the bonding is predominantly ionic. Overlap calculations on the energy of formation of a covalent bond using the $3s$ sodium orbital and $3p$ chlorine orbital show that a covalent bond would be much less favourable energetically.

It is also instructive to carry out a similar calculation for gaseous magnesium oxide on the assumption that it is $Mg^{2+}O^{2-}$. Here $I_M = 523$ kcal/mole, $E_X = -172$ kcal/mole (note the minus sign, which makes $-E_X$ positive) $z_1 = z_2 = 2$, and the observed internuclear separation is 1·75 Å; this leads to a value of $\Delta H = +88$ kcal/mole. Hence the formation of an ion pair would not be attended by an evolution of heat and the atoms are not bonded ionically; the gaseous compound behaves like a typical covalent molecule and its observed heat of formation from atoms is $\Delta H = -86$ kcal/mole. Such calculations can therefore be used as a rough criterion of the type of bonding which occurs in gaseous diatomic species.

We must now address ourselves to the problem of extending this theory of ion-pair formation in the gas phase to the case of an ionic crystal.

2.5. Lattice Energy of an Ideal Ionic Crystal

The lattice energy, U_L, of a crystal can be defined as the amount of energy required at absolute zero to convert 1 mole of the crystal into its constituent ions at infinite separation in the gas phase:

$$MX(cryst) \to M^+(g) + X^-(g); \quad -\Delta H = U_L \text{ kcal/mole} \quad (12)$$

This energy arises predominantly from the coulomb attraction and interatomic repulsion terms already considered but at temperatures above the absolute zero a further small increment $2RT$ must be added to represent the energy required to expand two moles of gas to infinitely small pressure; at room temperature $2RT = 1\cdot2$ kcal/mole. The main component of the lattice energy can be calculated in a straightforward way from the preceding theory. To see how this is done consider first the simpler case of an infinite one-dimensional lattice of alternating charges each distant r from its nearest neighbours.

For an isolated univalent ion pair the potential energy was given by equation (7)

$$\Phi = -\frac{e^2}{r} + be^{-r/\rho}$$

For a one-dimensional lattice the coulomb potential, Φ_c, at the cation indicated will be that due to two anions at a distance r, plus two cations at a distance $2r$, plus two anions at a distance $3r$ etc.

$$\Phi_c = -\frac{2e^2}{r} + \frac{2e^2}{2r} - \frac{2e^2}{3r} + \frac{2e^2}{4r} \cdots$$

$$= -\frac{2e^2}{r}(1 - \tfrac{1}{2} + \tfrac{1}{3} - \tfrac{1}{4} + \ldots)$$

17

c

The term in parentheses is simply $\ln 2 = 0.69$, hence

$$\Phi_c = -\frac{1.38\,e^2}{r}$$

The effect of all the ions in the linear lattice is simply to increase the coulomb potential energy by a factor of 1.38 over that due to a single ion pair. A similar argument applies to the repulsion energy, Φ_r, except that there, since the repulsive forces diminish exponentially and are of such short range, they become negligibly small after the first nearest neighbours:

$$\Phi_r = +2b\,e^{-r/\rho} + (2b\,e^{-2r/\rho} + 2b\,e^{-3r/\rho} + \ldots)$$

$$\sim 2b\,e^{-r/\rho}$$

Hence $\Phi = \Phi_c + \Phi_r = -1.38\,e^2/r + 2b\,e^{-r/\rho}$, and, using the relation that $(\partial\Phi/\partial r)_{r=r_0} = 0$, we obtain for the potential at the cation considered

$$\Phi_0 = \frac{-1.38\,e^2}{r_0}\left(1 - \frac{\rho}{r_0}\right) \tag{13}$$

Apart from the charges z_1 and z_2 which were omitted for simplicity, this expression differs from equation (10) only by the scaling factor 1.38. This factor is called the Madelung constant and is given the symbol A; its numerical value depends only on the geometry of the lattice and is independent of the charges and internuclear distances.

It can be seen in this way that the whole of the theory of the ion-pair developed in the preceding sections can be taken over directly for the case of ionic lattices simply by putting in the appropriate Madelung constant and scaling up by Avogadro's number N_0 to get from one ion pair to one gramme-mole of ion pairs. The lattice energy is then given by

$$U_L = [-N_0\Phi_0]_{\text{cryst}} = \frac{N_0 A z_1 z_2\,e^2}{r_0}\left(1 - \frac{\rho}{r_0}\right) \tag{14}$$

The theoretical calculation of lattice energies for simple crystals was first developed by Born and Landé and by Madelung in 1918. Some values of the Madelung constant for typical crystal structures are given in *Table 2.3*. More extensive compilations are given in the references.[1, 2] Care must be taken in using these data because different authors use various conventions about the inclusion or exclusion of the charges z_1, z_2 in their calculations. Similarly some authors calculate A in terms of the unit cell dimensions rather than the internuclear distance r_0. For example, on the unit-cell basis, the Madelung constant for the caesium-chloride-type structure is 2·03536, i.e. 1·76267 $(\sqrt{3})/2$, the factor $(\sqrt{3})/2$ being the ratio of the distance $r_0(Cs^+ - Cl^-)$ to the unit cell constant $a_0(Cl^- - Cl^-)$.

Table 2.3
Some Madelung constants

Structure type	A	Structure type	A	Structure type	A
CsCl	1·76267	CaF_2	5·03879	TiO_2 (rutile, $M^{2+}X_2^-$)	4·816
NaCl	1·74756	$CaCl_2$	4·730	TiO_2 (anatase, $M^{2+}X_2^-$)	4·800
ZnS (wurtzite)	1·64132	$CdCl_2$	4·489	SiO_2 (β-quartz, $M^{2+}X_2^-$)	4·4394
ZnS (sphalerite)	1·63805	CdI_2	4·383	Al_2O_3 (corundum)	25·0312
PdO ($c/a = 2\cdot0$)	1·60494	Cu_2O	4·44249		

Further complications arise in those crystal structures where more than one parameter can vary, e.g. the c/a ratio in tetragonal crystals, and in ternary compounds such as perovskites ABO_3 where the charges on A and B, and hence the Madelung constant (with respect to a_0), can vary, e.g. $NaTaO_3$ (58·53535), $SrTiO_3$ (49·50976), $LaAlO_3$ (44·55489). Here the Madelung constant diminishes the less the disparity between the two cationic charges.

Let us apply the lattice energy equation (14) to crystalline sodium chloride and magnesium oxide which were considered earlier as gaseous ion-pairs and which both have the sodium chloride structure. For both compounds $N_0 = 6\cdot023 \times 10^{23}$, $A = 1\cdot748$, $e = 4\cdot803 \times 10^{-10}$ e.s.u., 1 kcal $= 4\cdot184 \times 10^{10}$ erg, 1 Å $= 10^{-8}$ cm, and ρ can be taken as 0·345. For sodium chloride $z_1 = z_2 = 1$ and $r_0 = 2\cdot814$Å whence $U_L(NaCl) = 181\cdot0$ kcal/mole, and the energy of formation from the isolated gaseous atoms is

$$\Delta H(NaCl) = I_M - E_X - U_L = -148\cdot0 \text{ kcal/mole}$$

For magnesium oxide $z_1 = z_2 = 2$ and $r_0 = 2\cdot102$Å whence $U_L(MgO) = 923\cdot3$ kcal/mole and the energy of formation from the isolated gaseous atom is

$$\Delta H(MgO) = 523 + 172 - 923 = -228 \text{ kcal/mole}$$

It can be seen that the 75 per cent increase in coulombic attraction due to the Madelung term ensures that crystalline magnesium oxide, unlike the gaseous species, is effectively ionic.

19

More refined calculations of lattice energies will be deferred until Section 2.7 of this chapter.

2.6. The Born–Haber Cycle

In the discussion so far we have taken a rather arbitrary reference point for the zero of potential energy, viz. two isolated atoms infinitely separated in the gas phase. To proceed it is convenient to relate this arbitrary reference to the elements in their standard states so that lattice energies can be linked with other thermochemical data. This involves an application of the first law of thermodynamics to a thermochemical cycle first devised by Born in 1919 and developed by Haber in the same year. The heat of formation of a crystalline compound MX from its elements in their standard states, ΔH_f°, can be measured directly or can be calculated from the energy terms in a hypothetical reaction path which involves first subliming the metal to give gaseous metal atoms and dissociating the molecules of non-metal to give gaseous atoms, and then allowing these gaseous species to interact in the way discussed in the preceding sections. The two reaction paths are indicated in the subjoined diagram in which S is the sublimation energy of the metal and D is the dissociation energy of X_2.

$$M(\text{cryst}) + \tfrac{1}{2}X_2(g) \xrightarrow{S \,+\, \tfrac{1}{2}D} M(g) + X(g)$$

$$\Delta H_f^\circ \downarrow \qquad\qquad \downarrow +I_M \quad \downarrow -E_X$$

$$MX(\text{cryst}) \xleftarrow{\;-U_L\;} M^+(g) + X^-(g)$$

In this diagram, $+$ means heat absorbed, $-$ means heat evolved, and expansion terms (nRT) have been neglected as being within the experimental error of the quantities involved. From Hess's law:

$$\Delta H_f^\circ = S + \tfrac{1}{2}D + I_M - E_X - U_L \tag{15}$$

The equation can readily be generalized for the heat of formation of compounds MX_n:

$$\Delta H_f^\circ(MX_n) = S + \frac{n}{2}D + \sum_{1 \to n} I_M - nE_X - U_L \tag{16}$$

where $\sum$ indicates the sum of the first n ionization potentials of M. The Born–Haber cycle has several applications which are indicated below.

2.6.1. Determination of E_X and U_L

When the equation was first derived the first four terms in equation (15) were known experimentally but there were no values for E_X or

U_L. The original application of the equation was to determine electron affinities, using estimated values of the lattice energy calculated as in the preceding section. Approximate constancy of E_X for a series of compounds having a common anion, X, could then be taken as indicating that the computed lattice energies were at least self-consistent. A typical set of data will suffice to indicate the procedure (*Table 2.4*).

Table 2.4
Calculation of electron affinity from Born–Haber cycle (all energies in kcal/mole)

Compound	$-\Delta H_f^\circ$	S	$\frac{1}{2}D$	I_M	U_L	E_X
LiCl	97·7	33·2	29·0	124·3	200·2	84·0
NaCl	98·2	24·0	29·0	118·5	183·5	86·2
KCl	104·2	19·4	29·0	100·1	167·9	84·8
RbCl	102·9	18·6	29·0	96·3	162·0	84·8
CsCl	103·5	16·8	29·0	89·8	153·1	86·0

Mean 85·2 ± 1·2

It can be seen that, although the standard heats of formation ΔH_f°, vary over a range of 6·5 kcal/mole, the sublimation energies, S, vary by 16·4 kcal/mole, the ionization potentials, I_M, by 34·5 kcal/mole and the computed lattice energies,[1] U_L, by 47·1 kcal/mole, yet the calculated value for the electron affinity of chlorine, E_X, is constant to within ±1·2 kcal/mole. It is also close to the 'best' selected modern value of 85·5 ± 1·5 kcal/mole given in *Table 2.2*.

Now that reliable experimental values of electron affinities are becoming available, the Born–Haber cycle can be used conversely to calculate 'experimental' values of the lattice energy. These values, which depend only on experimentally measured quantities and the first law of thermodynamics, can then be compared with the values calculated by the Born theory of lattice energy. Systematic discrepancies are noticed which can be minimized by the more refined lattice energy calculations mentioned in section 2.7.

2.6.2. *Stability of Hypothetical Compounds*

A third application of the Born–Haber cycle is to calculate the energy of formation of hypothetical ionic compounds in order to see if they may conceivably exist. This technique was first suggested by Grimm in 1923 and has been developed extensively since. For example, if neon chloride were to exist as an ionic compound

---

[1] Huggins, M. L., *J. chem. Phys.*, **5** (1937) 143

Ne^+Cl^- it would be a simple matter to calculate its lattice energy on the reasonable assumptions that the compound would have an NaCl-type structure and that the ionic radius of Ne^+ would be similar to that of Na^+ but perhaps slightly smaller. As the ionization potential of neon is well known all the terms on the right hand side of equation (15) are known and the heat of formation can be calculated. The value obtained is $\Delta H_f^\circ(NeCl) = +246$ kcal/mole indicating, as expected, that the compound can not exist as an ionic crystal because of the impossibly high entropy term which would be required to make ΔG_f° negative ($\Delta G = \Delta H - T\Delta S$). A term-by-term comparison with sodium chloride shows that it is the extremely high ionization potential of neon which is the crucial factor (the sublimation energy of neon is taken as zero because it is a gas at room temperature):

	S	$\frac{1}{2}D_{Cl_2}$	I_M	$-E_{Cl}$	$-U_L$	ΔH_f°(calc.)
NaCl	24·0	29·0	118·5	−85·5	−183·5	−97·5
NeCl	0	29·0	498·2	−85·5	ca. −196	ca. +246

The heats of formation of several other hypothetical and real compounds are listed in *Table 2.5* and a more extensive compilation is given in Waddington's review cited at the end of this chapter.[1] It can be seen that, whenever the formation of a compound involves

Table 2.5
Heats of formation of some hypothetical and real compounds (ΔH_f° in kcal/mole)

NeCl	+246						
NaCl	−98	$NaCl_2$	+513				
MgCl	−30	$MgCl_2$	−153	$MgCl_3$	+200		
AlCl	−45	$AlCl_2$	−65	$AlCl_3$	−166	$AlCl_4$	+840

the breaching of an inert-gas core (e.g. NeCl, $NaCl_2$, $MgCl_3$, $AlCl_4$) the compound is too highly endothermic to exist, due to the very high ionization energies involved. By contrast, lower valent compounds such as MgCl, AlCl, and $AlCl_2$ when considered as typical ionic compounds are always formed with evolution of heat from their elements. However, the compounds are unstable with respect to disproportionation and so normally can not be isolated.

For example, *Table 2.5* indicates the following heats of reaction:

$$2Mg(cryst) + Cl_2(g) = 2MgCl(cryst); \Delta H° = -60 \text{ kcal/mole}$$
$$Mg(cryst) + Cl_2(g) = MgCl_2(cryst); \Delta H° = -153 \text{ kcal/mole}$$

Hence $2MgCl(cryst) = Mg(cryst) + MgCl_2(cryst); \Delta H_{disprop} = -93$ kcal/mole. Likewise from *Table 2.5*, the heats of disproportionation of AlCl and $AlCl_2$ are:

$$3AlCl(cryst) = 2Al(cryst) + AlCl_3(cryst);$$
$$\Delta H_{disprop} = -31 \text{ kcal/mole}$$
$$3AlCl_2(cryst) = Al(cryst) + 2AlCl_3(cryst);$$
$$\Delta H_{disprop} = -137 \text{ kcal/mole}$$

It is therefore most important to distinguish between heats of formation from the element and stability since, quite apart from entropy effects, a compound may be formed with evolution of energy from its elements yet still be unstable with respect to disproportionation.

It is clear from the foregoing discussion of the factors affecting the stability of ionic compounds in unusual oxidation states, that divalent compounds of the alkali metals would be favoured the lower the second stage ionization potential of the metal and the greater the lattice energy term (i.e. the smaller the internuclear distance in the crystal). The trends discussed in Section 2.1 (p. 9) suggest that caesium would be the most favourable alkali metal to doubly ionize, and the smallest internuclear distance would then be attained with the fluoride as anion. Born–Haber calculations show that CsF_2 could indeed be formed exothermically from its elements but once again the compound is unstable with respect to disproportionation:

$$Cs + F_2 = CsF_2; \quad \Delta H_f° = -30 \text{ kcal/mole}$$
$$CsF_2 = CsF + \tfrac{1}{2}F_2; \Delta H_{disprop} = -97 \text{ kcal/mole}$$

An improvement would result if the moderately low second stage ionization potential of the metal atom could be allied to an ionic radius smaller than that of caesium. The element copper immediately suggests itself since less energy is required to breach the d^{10} core than to ionize the inert-gas core (see Appendix). These factors lead to the well-known stability of the cupric halides,

e.g. $$Cu + F_2 = CuF_2; \quad \Delta H_f° = -127 \text{ kcal/mole}$$

Even with the larger ion Ag^{2+} the heat of formation is -49 kcal/mole and the heat of disproportionation is approximately zero, so that the

23

compound can exist. However, when larger anions are used, the diminishing lattice energy leads to calculated heats of formation which imply instability,

e.g.

$$AgCl_2 + 23\,kcal/mole,\ AgBr_2 + 40\,kcal/mole,\ AgI_2 + 67\,kcal/mole$$

Here it is the small size of the fluoride ion which ensures stability of the higher-valent compound. Parallel calculations on CuF show that this compound (like AuF) is unstable towards disproportionation[1] whereas, of course, AgF is quite stable.

It can be seen that the actual oxidation state adopted by a particular element in its ionic compounds is a result of the subtle interplay of several factors: energy of ionization, enhanced coulomb attraction of multivalent ions, dependence of lattice energy on ionic radii, and disproportionation energies to neighbouring oxidation states. When successive stages of ionization require only moderate additional expenditure of energy this may be approximately compensated for by the enhanced coulomb attraction of the higher charges and a series of stable valency states may result. This is typically the situation with the transition elements.[2] Without doing appropriate calculations it is frequently not clear from the electronic structure of the metal atom (which refers to the ground state configuration in the gas phase) just what degree of ionization is to be expected. For example, many of the lanthanides have the configuration $4f^n6s^2$ but form tervalent ions M^{3+} ($4f^{n-1}$) because it is at this point that the most favourable balance of energies is obtained.

Calculations of lattice energies and predictions of chemical stability played a large part in the initial development of inert-gas chemistry. Crystallographic analysis and magnetic susceptibility measurements on the newly prepared compound O_2PtF_6 suggested that it was largely ionic, $O_2^+PtF_6^-$; since the ionization potential of molecular oxygen (281·3 kcal/mole) is close to that of xenon (279·7 kcal/mole) Bartlett considered that xenon might similarly be oxidized by gaseous PtF_6 and direct reaction of the two gases led to the formation of the orange crystalline compound $XePtF_6$.[3]

---

[1] Waddington, T. C., *Trans. Faraday Soc.*, **55** (1959) 1531

[2] Barber, M., Linnett, J. W. and Taylor, N. H., *J. chem. Soc.* (1961) 3323

[3] Bartlett, N. and Lohmann, D. H., *Proc. chem. Soc.* (1962) 115; Bartlett, N., *Proc. chem. Soc.* (1962) 218

2.6.3. *Further Applications*

Further applications of the Born–Haber cycle are to the determination of proton affinities, heats of complex ion formation, and hydration energies. These applications are quite straightforward as is apparent from the following cycles. The classical example of the determination of a proton affinity, P, is the case of the ammonium ion:

$$\underbrace{\tfrac{1}{2}N_2(g) + 2H_2(g) + \tfrac{1}{2}X_2(g)}_{\Delta H_f^\circ} \xrightarrow{-\Delta H_f^\circ (NH_3) + \tfrac{1}{2}D_{H_2} + \tfrac{1}{2}D_{X_2}} NH_3(g) + H(g) + X(g)$$

with cycle terms: ΔH_f°, $NH_4X(cryst)$, $-U_L$, I_H, $NH_3(g) + H^+(g)$, $-E_X$, $P(NH_3)$, $NH_4^+(g) + X^-(g)$

Using calculated values for the lattice energy of ammonium chloride, bromide, and iodide, and experimental values for all the other terms gives the proton affinity of ammonia, $P(NH_3)$, as 209·4, 210·5, and 208·5 kcal/mole respectively.

The value calculated from data on ammonium fluoride differs somewhat because of hydrogen bonding in the crystal. Other proton affinities calculated in a similar way are assembled in *Table 2.6*. The trends are obvious.

Table 2.6
Proton affinities of some molecules and ions

Group	NH_3	NH_2^-	NH^{2-}
P kcal/mole	209	393	613
Group	H_2O	OH^-	O^{2-}
P kcal/mole	182	375	554
Group		SH^-	S^{2-}
P kcal/mole		342	550

(From Waddington, T. C., *Adv. inorg. Chem. Radiochem.*, **1** (1959) 157)

Analogous cycles lead to the heats of formation of complex anions shown in *Table 2.7*; such values are particularly helpful in monitoring calculations of reorganization energies which accompany changes in symmetry during reactions of the type

$$BF_3(g) + F^-(g) = BF_4^-(g)$$

Hydration energies of ions can be obtained by a subsidiary cycle in which the crystalline compound is either dissolved directly (which gives its heat of solution) or is first conceptually dissociated into

Table 2.7
Heats of formation of complex anions in the gas phase

Acceptor	Ligand	Complex	ΔH kcal/mole
BF_3	F^-	BF_4^-	-76
BH_3	H^-	BH_4^-	-75
HF	F^-	HF_2^-	-58
SO_3	O^{2-}	SO_4^{2-}	-314
SeO_3	O^{2-}	SeO_4^{2-}	-339

free gaseous ions (lattice energy) and then dissolved to give the same final state (heat of hydration of ions, ΔH_h):

$$MX(cryst) \xrightarrow{\;\Delta H_{soln}\;} M^+(aq) + X^-(aq)$$

$$U_L \searrow \qquad \nearrow \Delta H_h(M^+) + \Delta H_h(X^-)$$

$$M^+(g) + X^-(g)$$

Various semi-empirical methods have been devised for apportioning the sum of the ion hydration energies between the individual ions[1] and several self-consistent sets of values have been derived. One set which was recently derived[2] on the simple assumption that $\Delta H_h Cs^+(g) = \Delta H_h I^-(g)$ is given in *Table 2.8*. These values lie within a few kcal of those calculated on the basis of much more sophisticated models and can be taken as a reliable indication of the true values. The trends are obvious and can be interpreted in terms of ionic radius, ionic charge, presence of an inert-gas or d^{10} core, etc. Such heats of hydration, in conjunction with entropy data, give a valuable insight into the solubility of ionic crystals, but this topic falls outside the scope of the present discussion.

[1] Halliwell, H. F. and Nyburg, S. C., *Trans. Faraday Soc.*, **59**, (1963) 1126
[2] Vasil'ev, V. P., Zolobarev, E. K., Kapustinskii, A. F., Mischenko, K. P., Podgornaya, E. A. and Yatsimirskii, K. B. *Russ. J. phys. Chem.*, **34** (1960) 840; as recalculated by Ladd, M. F. C. and Lee, W. H. *Prog. Solid St. Chem.*, **2** (1965) 378

Table 2.8
Heats of hydration of individual ions ($-\Delta H_h$ kcal/mole)

Univalent cations		Bivalent cations		Tervalent cations		Monatomic anions		Polyatomic anions	
Li^+	127	Be^{2+}	601					OH^-	122
Na^+	101	Mg^{2+}	467	Al^{3+}	1125	F^-	116	$CH_3CO_2^-$	101
K^+	81	Ca^{2+}	386	Ga^{3+}	1131	Cl^-	84	HCO_2^-	99
Rb^+	75	Sr^{2+}	353	Tl^{3+}	1012	Br^-	76	HCO_3^-	91
Cs^+	67	Ba^{2+}	320	Ce^{3+}	860	I^-	67	CN^-	83
		Ra^{2+}	310					CNO^-	93
Cu^+	146	Zn^{2+}	496	Sc^{3+}	958	S^{2-}	320	CNS^-	74
Ag^+	117	Cd^{2+}	439	La^{3+}	796			HS^-	82
Tl^+	82	Hg^{2+}	443	Fe^{3+}	1056			NO_2^-	98
				Quadrivalent cations				NO_3^-	74
H^+	265	Sn^{2+}	379	Ce^{4+}	1566			ClO_3^-	69
H_3O^+	110	Pb^{2+}	362	Th^{4+}	994			ClO_4^-	54
NH_4^+	78							MnO_4^-	59
								SO_4^{2-}	265

Transition Metal Cations $-\Delta H_h$ (kcal/mole)	Cr^{2+}	Mn^{2+}	Fe^{2+}	Co^{2+}	Ni^{2+}	Cu^{2+}	Zn^{2+}
	450	449	467	499	511	509	496

2.7. Further Refinements in Lattice-energy Calculations

The preceding section has shown the importance of having reliable methods for calculating precise lattice energies in order that reliable predictions can be made about the stability of compounds, etc. This section examines ways in which the simple procedure so far used to calculate lattice energies can be refined. This will enable us to draw conclusions as to why, in certain cases there are considerable discrepancies between observed and calculated values and why, in other circumstances, the calculations are apparently much better than might have been expected. We will also discuss methods for estimating lattice energies even when the crystal structure and internuclear distances are not known experimentally or when the shape of the ions themselves makes it unreasonable to consider them as spherical (e.g. linear CNO^-, planar NO_3^-). The sequence of presentation will be to discuss first, the additional terms such as London dispersion energy and zero-point energy which must be considered even for ideally ionic lattices with spherical ions; secondly, the crystal-field stabilization energy of non-spherical ions of transition elements; thirdly, the deviations from ideal ionic behaviour which arise as a result of polarization and covalency effects;

27

and finally, Kapustinskii's generalized method for estimating lattice energies of complex structures.

2.7.1. Extended Lattice-energy Equations

The original Born–Landé equation expressed the lattice energy as the sum of a coulomb attractive term and a term incorporating the repulsion energies as a function of $1/r^n$ where n is an integer between 5 and 12:

$$U_L = \frac{N_0 A z_1 z_2 e^2}{r} - \frac{N_0 B}{r^n} \tag{17}$$

This was modified by Born and Mayer to account for the exponential decay of the mutually repelling radial wave functions:

$$U_L = \frac{N_0 A z_1 z_2 e^2}{r} - N_0 B e^{-r/\rho} \tag{18}$$

In addition, the ions in a crystal will be in vibratory motion and this leads to a further induced dipole-dipole attractive force due to the mutual synchronous polarization of the ions. London showed that this force, which also leads to the van der Waals attraction between gaseous atoms or molecules, gives rise to an attractive energy which depends on the polarizabilities of the ions and on the inverse sixth power of their internuclear separation. This increases the lattice energy by an amount $N_0 C/r^6$. There is a further term incorporating the zero-point energy of the crystal; this arises from the quantum-mechanical theory of lattice vibrations because, at absolute zero, it is not possible for all vibrations to pack into the lowest single vibrational mode of the crystal—they must be placed in the lowest sequence of allowed energy levels. On the (rather unjustified) assumption that the ionic crystal behaves as a simple Debye solid, the zero-point energy lowers the lattice energy by an amount $2.25\,N_0 h v_{max}$, where v_{max} is the frequency of the highest occupied vibrational mode in the crystal. The lattice energy equation then becomes:

$$U_L = \frac{N_0 A z_1 z_2 e^2}{r} - N_0 B\, e^{-r/\rho} + \frac{N_0 C}{r^6} - \frac{9}{4} N_0 h v_{max} \tag{19}$$

An idea of the relative magnitude of these various terms can be obtained from the extensive calculations of several authors.[1]

[1] Mayer, J. E. and Helmholz, L. Z. Physik, **75** (1932) 19; Mayer, J. E. and Maltbie, M. McC., Z. Physik, **75** (1932) 748; Huggins, M. L. J. chem. Phys., **5** (1937) 143

Typical values for our earlier model compounds are:

	$N_0 A z_1 z_2 e^2/r$	$N_0 B\,e^{-r/\rho}$	$N_0 C/r^6$	$2{\cdot}25 N_0 h\nu_{max}$	U_L
NaCl	$+205{\cdot}6$	$-23{\cdot}6$	$+2{\cdot}9$	$-1{\cdot}7$	$183{\cdot}2$
MgO	$+1108$	-167	$+1{\cdot}5$	$-4{\cdot}4$	938

More extensive tabulations indicate that the London attractive energy (expressed as a percentage of the total lattice energy) rises from $\sim 0{\cdot}5$ per cent for LiF to ~ 5 per cent for CsI, whereas the zero-point energy term drops from $\sim 1{\cdot}5$ per cent for LiF to $\sim 0{\cdot}5$ per cent for CsI. For divalent metal oxides and sulphides the London term is normally $<0{\cdot}5$ per cent and the zero-point energy about $0{\cdot}2$–$0{\cdot}5$ per cent of the total lattice energy. As these two terms act in opposite directions they have an almost negligible net influence on the lattice energy particularly when uncertainties in the internuclear distance r_0 and the Born repulsion exponent ρ are considered.

A more recent extension also includes quadrupole interactions, which are inversely proportional to r^8 and, using the condition that $(\partial U/\partial r) = 0$ at $r = r_0$ one obtains the equation of Ladd and Lee[1]:

$$
U_L = \frac{N_0 A z_1 z_2 e^2}{r_0}\left(1 - \frac{\rho}{r_0}\right) + \frac{N_0 C}{r_0{}^6}\left(1 - \frac{6\rho}{r_0}\right)
$$
$$
+ \frac{N_0 D}{r_0{}^8}\left(1 - \frac{8\rho}{r_0}\right) - \frac{9}{4}N_0 h\nu_{max} \qquad (20)
$$

For cubic crystals the value of ρ/r is related to the isotropic compressibility $\beta = (\partial^2 U/\partial V^2)/V$ and the molar volume of the crystal V_0 by the expression

$$
\frac{\rho}{r} = \frac{\left[\dfrac{Ae^2}{r_0} + \dfrac{6C}{r_0{}^6} + \dfrac{8D}{r_0{}^8}\right]}{\left[\dfrac{9V_0}{\beta} + \dfrac{2Ae^2}{r_0} + \dfrac{42C}{r_0{}^6} + \dfrac{72D}{r_0{}^8}\right]}
$$

Fortunately the correction coefficients C, D and β do not need to be known with great precision. For example, for potassium chloride,

[1] Ladd, M. F. C. and Lee, W. H., *Trans. Faraday Soc.*, **54** (1958) 34; *J. inorg. nucl. Chem.*, **11** (1959) 264

a 50 per cent error in C and D affects the lattice energy by only 0·5 per cent and a 20 per cent variation in β produces only a 2·5 per cent variation in a lattice energy of 200 kcal/mole.

The preceding treatment applies only to spherical ions where it is possible to define a unique radius r_0. When the ions are polyatomic and non-spherical some assumption has to be made about their 'repulsion envelopes' so that radii in different directions can be assigned. The azide ion $N_3{}^-$ and the bifluoride ion $HF_2{}^-$ have been treated in this way.[1] Even monatomic ions may differ from spherical symmetry if they contain incomplete electron shells and this situation will be considered in the next section.

2.7.2. Crystal-field Stabilization Energy

Incompletely filled p orbitals usually result in gross deviations from simple ionic bonding because the overlap of the unfilled orbitals leads to covalent interactions. Incompletely filled $4f$ orbitals are usually well-shielded from the crystal field of surrounding ions and such ions behave as essentially spherical. There is a somewhat larger interaction for $5f$ electrons, but the most clearly defined effects are seen with incompletely filled d orbitals.[2]

When a transition element ion is surrounded octahedrally by six anions the d_γ orbitals $(d_{x^2-y^2}, d_{z^2})$ which are directed towards the anions are destabilized with respect to the d_ε orbitals (d_{xy}, d_{yz}, d_{zx}) which point in between the neighbouring anions. The energy differences from the weighted mean are then as shown in *Figure 2.3*. Neglecting for the moment the inter-electronic repulsive forces, an electron in a d_ε orbital is stabilized by an amount $4Dq$ and an

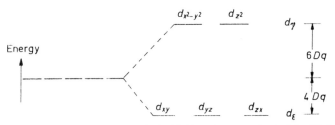

Figure 2.3. Influence of an octahedral field on the energy level of d-orbitals

[1] Gray, P. and Waddington, T. C., *Proc. R. Soc.*, **A235** (1956) 481; Waddington, T. C., *Trans. Faraday Soc.*, **54** (1958) 25

[2] Orgel, L. E. *An Introduction to Transition-Metal Chemistry: Ligand-Field Theory*, Methuen, London, 1963

electron in a d_γ orbital is destabilized by an amount $6Dq$. For typical hydrates and oxides of divalent first row transition elements $10Dq$ is of the order of 20–35 kcal/mole and for the corresponding trivalent ions it is approximately 40–60 kcal/mole. Values of $10Dq$ for second and third row transition elements are substantially higher than for the first row ions and it is clear that crystal field effects may make an appreciable contribution to the total lattice energy. *Table 2.9* lists the stabilization resulting from various numbers of d electrons. If the value of $10Dq$ is less than the mutual electrostatic repulsion energy of two electrons occupying one and the same d orbital, then as many electrons as possible will remain unpaired (high-spin case). If $10Dq$ is larger than the coulomb repulsion the

Table 2.9
Crystal-field stabilization energies (c.f.s.e.) of d-orbitals in an octahedral field

number of d electrons	0	1	2	3	4	5	6	7	8	9	10
high-spin c.f.s.e. (in Dq)	0	4	8	12	6	0	4	8	12	6	0
low-spin c.f.s.e. (in Dq)	0	4	8	12	16	20	24	18	12	6	0
difference (in Dq)	0	0	0	0	10	20	20	10	0	0	0

electrons will tend to pair (low-spin case). The difference between these two states is also given in *Table 2.9*. It is found in Chapter 5 that the difference in crystal-field stabilization energy of various transition metal ions in octahedral and in tetrahedral fields is an important factor in deciding the detailed crystal structure of some compounds such as spinels (p. 98). Meanwhile, it is sufficient to note that, for high-spin ions, there is no crystal-field stabilization energy for d^0, d^5 and d^{10} configurations which are spherically symmetrical; the actual stabilization for other configurations will depend on the particular value of $10Dq$ for the ion considered. However, the broad trend is quite clear, as illustrated in *Figure 2.4* which plots the actual lattice energies of divalent halides of first row transition metals as calculated from experimental data using the Born–Haber cycle. The stabilization varies from about 20 to 50 kcal/mole and amounts to about 3–8 per cent of the total lattice energy. As expected from the spectrochemical series the stabilization increases in the sequence $F < Cl < Br < I$.

31

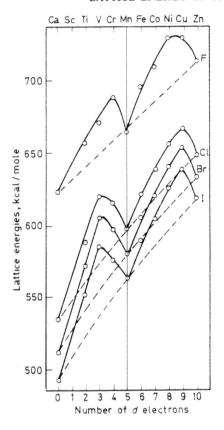

Figure 2.4. Crystal field stabilization energy of the dihalides of first-row transition elements

(After T. C. Waddington[1])

2.7.3. *Deviations due to Polarization Effects*

Polarization is a distortion of the electronic charge density around an ion and it can arise from a variety of interrelated causes. In its most extreme form polarization results in the effective removal of an electron from an anion towards the cation and the formation of a covalent bond. Polarization can thus be considered as the link between purely ionic interaction on the one hand and purely covalent bonding on the other. It will only be possible to touch on some aspects here; fuller treatments will be found in the books by Wells and by Evans mentioned at the end of this Chapter and there is a particularly perceptive discussion in Volume I of Phillips and Williams.

Polarization is more extensive the lower the coordination number and it also depends on both the polarizing power and the polarizability of the ions in the structure. Polarizing power increases the

32

smaller the ion, the higher its charge, and the less effectively its nucleus is shielded by the extranuclear electrons. Small, highly-charged cations therefore have considerable polarizing power and d^{10} ions are more highly polarizing than inert gas ions. By contrast polarizability, or ease of distortion, will be greatest for large ions (usually anions) with loosely bound electrons. Various quantitative measures of polarizability have been proposed from time to time. Goldschmidt originally suggested that polarizing power could be measured by the surface potential of an ion ze/r^2; this quantifies the charge and size criteria mentioned above but does not explain why Cu^+, which has the same formal charge and radius as Na^+, is much more highly polarizing. The model can be retained by introducing an 'effective' charge z_{eff} which is greater for the d^{10} ion due to incomplete shielding of the higher nuclear charge but it is more satisfactory to use some empirical measure of this 'effective' charge. One such attempt[1] defines a 'shielding efficiency' in terms of the function $5z^{1.27}/(I_M r^{\frac{1}{2}})$. However, detailed empirical formulae are less important for our present purpose than an appreciation of the broad trend of results.

Quantitative scales for polarizability have also been devised; this distortion in an electrostatic field is related to polarizability in an electromagnetic field so that molar refraction of ions can be used as a measure of polarizability. More sophisticated treatments led to scales such as that set out in *Table 2.10* which gives the

Table 2.10
Polarizability of some ions (in arbitrary units, $F = 1.0$)

Electron con-figuration	Polarizability												
helium					Li^+	0.08	Be^{2+}	0.03	B^{3+}	0.01			
neon	O^{2-}	3.1	F^-	1.0	Na^+	0.2	Mg^{2+}	0.1	Al^{3+}	0.07	Si^{4+}	0.04
argon	S^{2-}	7.3	Cl^-	3.1	K^+	0.9	Ca^{2+}	0.6	Sc^{3+}	0.4	Ti^{4+}	0.3
krypton	Se^{2-}	7.5	Br^-	4.2	Rb^+	1.8	Sr^{2+}	1.4	Y^{3+}	1.0		
xenon	Te^{2-}	9.6	I^-	6.3	Cs^+	2.8	Ba^{2+}	2.1	La^{3+}	1.6	Ce^{4+}	1.2

polarizability of various isoelectronic sequences of ions. It is evident that polarizability diminishes rapidly with decrease in radius and with increase in positive charge within each horizontal row, and that large anions are the most readily polarizable species.

[1] Ahrens, L. H., *Nature*, **174** (1954) 644

Polarization of an ionic structure always leads to a decrease in interatomic distance and to an increase in lattice energy. Considerable discrepancies between calculated lattice energies and experimental lattice energies can be taken as indicating polarization effects and a tendency towards covalency. Paradoxically, however, these deviations are not directly related to the degree of covalency since the ionic model is 'self-compensating' and usually gives better values than might have been anticipated. This arises because of the form of the coulomb term $z_1 z_2 e^2/r$ as can be seen from the following oversimplified example. Consider a hypothetical, purely ionic, divalent compound $M^{2+}X^{2-}$ with an interionic separation of 2 Å; then, in appropriate units, the coulomb energy will be proportional to $z_1 z_2/r = 2$. Suppose now, that the compound, instead of being purely ionic is 10 per cent covalent—this will raise the lattice energy to, say 2·2 units; the ionic contribution to this will be $1·8 \times 1·8/2 = 1·6$ units, the discrepancy being 0·6 units. However, in an *actual* calculation of the lattice energy the formal charges $+2$ and -2 would be used (since the actual charges are rarely known) and, in addition the tendency to covalency will have reduced the internuclear distance from its value in the hypothetical, purely ionic crystal. If, in the actual crystal the internuclear distance had diminished to 1·8 Å, say, then the calculated lattice energy would be $2 \times 2/1·8 = 2·2$ units, close to the observed value. Thus, agreement between observed and calculated lattice energies does not necessarily indicate pure ionic bonding because the calculations use the empirical internuclear distances and the formal charges. For the same reason it is incorrect to use deviations between observed and calculated lattice energies as a *quantitative* measure of the degree of covalency in a crystal though such discrepancies may legitimately be used to infer the *presence* of polarization effects and partial covalency. A convincing example is quoted by Phillips and Williams who point out that if metallic lithium were considered to be a purely ionic crystal Li^+Li^- then, using the observed interatomic distance, the computed lattice energy is very close to the observed lattice energy. Even more dramatically, the energy of formation of gaseous BF_3 calculated on the basis of a planar triangular array of ions B^{3+} and $3F^-$ is within 3 per cent of the observed energy, and similar ionic calculations for SiF_4, PF_5, SF_6 and other covalent halides yield values within 5 per cent of the correct energy.[1]

In addition to affecting the lattice energy of a compound (and also reducing its solubility in polar solvents) polarization has

[1] Garrick, F. J., *Phil. Mag.*, **14**(1932) 914

marked effects on crystal structure and this aspect will be considered in Chapter 3 (p. 47).

2.7.4. Kapustinskii's Equation

The detailed calculation of the lattice energy of a compound requires a knowledge of its crystal structure in order that its Madelung constant and internuclear distances can be determined. Even when the structure is known it may involve non-spherical ions or be so complex as to render precise Madelung computations impracticable. In such cases it becomes desirable to have a general method for estimating lattice energies and the most satisfactory method is the semi-empirical approach of Kapustinskii. It was found that differences between the Madelung constant for a given crystal and that of the sodium-chloride structure were compensated by differences between the actual interionic distances and those calculated from tables of 6-coordinate ionic radii. Putting in numerical values for the constants in equation (14) p. 18 gives

$$U_L = 287.2 \frac{v z_1 z_2}{r_c + r_a} \left(1 - \frac{0.345}{r_c + r_a} \right)$$

where v is the number of ions in the formula (2 for NaCl, 3 for $CaCl_2$, etc.) and r_c and r_a are the formal 6-coordinate radii of the cation and the anion in ångstrom units. In cases where it can be checked against precise calculations of lattice energy this generalized

Table 2.11
Thermochemical radii of tetrahedral anions (in Å)

BF_4^-	2·28	BeF_4^-	2·45	ClO_4^-	2·36	IO_4^-	2·49	ClO_4^-	2·36
SO_4^{2-}	2·30	SeO_4^{2-}	2·43	TeO_4^{2-}	2·54	CrO_4^{2-}	2·40	MoO_4^{2-}	2·54
PO_4^{3-}	2·38	AsO_4^{3-}	2·48	SbO_4^{3-}	2·60	BiO_4^{3-}	2·68	SiO_4^{4-}	2·4

Table 2.12
Thermochemical radii of polyatomic anions (in Å)

OH^-	1·40	SH^-	1·95	SeH^-	2·15	CN^-	1·82	CNO^-	1·59	CNS^-	1·95
NH_2^-	1·30	NO_2^-	1·55	HCO_2^-	1·58	$CH_3CO_2^-$	1·58	HCO_3^-	1·63	picr.$^-$*	2·23
CO_3^{2-}	1·85	NO_3^-	1·89	ClO_3^-	2·00	BrO_3^-	1·91	IO_3^-	1·89	O_2^{2-}	1·80

* picr.$^-$ = 2,4,6,-$(NO_2)_3C_6H_2O^-$

equation has been found to be remarkably accurate. If the lattice energy is known from thermochemical cycles then the process can be inverted and 'thermochemical radii' of complex ions can be determined. Typical examples are given in Tables 2.11 and 2.12.

Likewise the radius of the monohydrated barium ion $[Ba(H_2O)]^{2+}$ was found to be 1.61 ± 0.01 Å. It should be emphasized that these radii only have significance in lattice-energy calculations by means of the Kapustinskii equation and do not carry any normal stereochemical significance. This can be seen from the fact that, for example, r_a for $CNS^- > CNO^- < CN^-$; $ClO_3^- > BrO_3^- > IO_3^-$; and $(NO_2)_3C_6H_2O^- < BF_4^-$.

Kapustinskii's equation has been criticized for emphasizing the sum of the radii ($r_c + r_a$) whereas in many ionic crystals the interatomic distances are determined predominantly by anion–anion contacts. However, it remains true that the equation gives an invaluable guide to lattice energies of complex compounds which are essentially ionic. It has also been used to predict the stable existence of several compoundss notably the lower-valent halides and chalcogenides of the lanthanide elements.[1]

References for Further Reading

1. Waddington, T. C., 'Lattice Energies and their Significance in Inorganic Chemistry', *Adv. inorg. Chem. Radiochem.*, 1 (1959) 157–221
2. Ladd, M. F. C. and Lee, W. H., 'Lattice Energies and Related Topics', *Prog. solid st. Chem.*, 1 (1963) 37–82; 2 (1965) 378–413
3. Kapustinskii, A. F., 'Lattice Energies of Ionic Crystals', *Q. Rev.*, 10 (1956) 283–294
4. Phillips, C. S. G. and Williams, R. J. P., *Inorganic Chemistry*, Vol. I, Chapter 5, Oxford University Press, 1966
5. Evans, R. C., *An Introduction to Crystal Chemistry* (2nd edn), Cambridge University Press, 1964
6. Wells, A. F., *Structural Inorganic Chemistry* (3rd edn), Oxford University Press, 1962
7. Ahrens, L. H. and Morris, D. F. C., 'Ionization Potentials and the Chemical Binding and Structure of Simple Inorganic Crystalline Compounds' Parts I and II, *J. inorg. nucl. Chem.*, 3 (1956) 263, 270
8. Waddington, T. C., 'Ionic Radii and the Method of the Undetermined Parameter', *Trans. Faraday Soc.*, 62 (1966) 1482

[1] Novikov, G. I. and Polyachenok, O. G., *Russ. J. inorg. Chem.*, 8 (1963) 816

3

THE SHAPE OF IONIC CRYSTALS

THREE dominant factors underlie the geometrical structure of ionic crystals:

(a) the electrostatic principle, that an ion surrounds itself with ions of opposite charge in such a way as to preserve macroscopic neutrality;
(b) the steric factor, which determines how sets of ions with differing radii can pack together to give a maximum binding energy;
(c) the effect of polarization in modifying the ideal structures derived on the assumption that ions are hard, impenetrable, non-distorted spheres.

The electrostatic principle is self-evident and calls for little comment at this stage though it will assume greater importance when non-stoichiometric compounds are being considered, since replacement of an ion by one with a different charge sometimes necessitates leaving vacant lattice sites (see Chapter 6). Discussion of steric factors requires some prior definition of the size of an ion and this will be treated in the next section. The effects of polarization will be discussed in Section 3.3 and this will be followed by two sections describing typical crystal structures.

3.1. Ionic Radii

X-ray structural analysis gives the internuclear distances in a crystal and the problem is how to apportion these distances between the anions and cations. It is important to emphasize that an ion does not have a unique radius as if it were a hard sphere. Quantum mechanics indicates that the electron distribution around an ion falls away as an exponential function of the radial distance and it becomes arbitrary to decide at what radius the ion is considered to have its exterior surface. Moreover, the electron distribution around an atom is deformable and the closeness of approach of a neighbouring ion will depend to some extent on the coordination number and on polarization effects. We have also seen that the radius of an ion with an incomplete d shell may be different in various directions depending on ligand-field effects. For these

37

reasons it is not possible to derive a single set of self-consistent ionic radii since the term itself has no precise physical meaning. Within these limitations, however, it is possible to indicate the effective dimensions of ions in given situations. Two types of method have been used to assign radii to ions. Wasastjerna (1923) apportioned the internuclear distances in the alkali halides in the ratio of the calculated molar refractivities of the ions; that is, he assumes the molar refractivity was proportional to the volume of an ion. This led to values of 1·33 Å for F^- and 1·32 Å for O^{2-} and these figures were adopted by Goldschmidt (1926) in his extensive tabulations. An alternative approach was adopted by Landé (1920). He assumed in the first instance that, in the lithium halides, the anions were in contact with each other and that this determined the unit cell dimensions. In a development of this method Landé considered the internuclear distances (in Å) in a series of compounds having the sodium chloride structure. Using more modern data:

| MgO 2·10 | MgS 2·59 | MgSe 2·72 |
| MnO 2·22 | MnS 2·61 | MnSe 2·72 |

He concluded that for the selenides, and probably also for the sulphides the anions were in contact. Hence, from the geometry of the crystal, $r(S^{2-}) = 2 \cdot 60/\sqrt{2} = 1 \cdot 84$ Å and $r(Se^{2-}) = 2 \cdot 72/\sqrt{2} = 1 \cdot 92$ Å. All other radii could then be obtained by simple arithmetic using sequences of compounds containing common ions. In a similar way Bragg (1927) derived the radius of the oxide ion by taking half the O—O distance in silicates: $r(O^{2-}) \sim 1 \cdot 35$ Å.

The most extensive compilation of radii is due to Pauling who used a flexible combination of interrelated criteria to derive a standard set of radii appropriate to 6-coordination.[1] He first considered those alkali halides which were composed of iso-electronic pairs of ions: NaF, KCl, RbBr, and CsI, together with Li_2O. For these ions the radius was taken to be inversely proportional to the effective nuclear charge operating on the extra-nuclear electrons. Z_{eff} equals the actual nuclear charge Z minus a screening effect S which was obtained partly by theoretical calculation, partly by interpretation of molar refractivities and partly from X-ray term values for atoms. Thus,

$$r = C_n/(Z - S)$$

[1] Pauling, L., *Nature of the Chemical Bond* (3rd edn), Cornell University Press, 1960

where C_n is a proportionality constant which depends on the principal quantum number of the outermost electron shell. For example, for the neon structure, $S = 4.52$ so that $Z_{eff}(Na^+) = 6.48$ and $Z_{eff}(F^-) = 4.48$; when the observed internuclear distance in NaF (2·31 Å) is apportioned in the inverse of this ratio the standard crystal radii are obtained as $r(Na^+) = 0.95$ Å and $r(F^-) = 1.36$ Å. The process can be continued with appropriate scaling factors for multivalent ions and Pauling also extended his list of radii by incorporating the empirical crystal radii of Goldschmidt, adjusted so as to be consistent with the value of 1·40 Å for O^{2-} since this gave better overall consistency than Goldschmidt's values based on Wasastjerna's figures of 1·32 Å for O^{2-} and 1·33 Å for F^-.

Pauling's values together with some more recent data are shown in *Table 3.1*. Several trends are immediately apparent:

(*a*) cations are normally smaller than anions, the only exceptions being the four largest cations (Rb^+, Cs^+, Fr^+, and Ra^{2+}) which are larger than the smallest anion, F^-;

(*b*) within each vertical group the radius increases with an increase in atomic number;

(*c*) within each horizontal isoelectronic sequence the radius decreases rapidly with increase in positive charge, e.g. from 0·95 Å for Na^+ to 0·26 Å for Cl^{7+};

(*d*) increase in negative charge in an isoelectronic sequence has less effect, particularly for the chalcogens when compared to the halogens;

(*e*) ions with a d^{10} configuration are smaller than the preceding equivalent cation having an inert gas configuration, e.g. Cu^+ 0·96 Å, K^+ 1·33 Å;

(*f*) ions carrying the same charge in a sequence of consecutive transition elements or lanthanides show a progressive diminution in radius;

(*g*) successive increases in the valency of a cation progressively decrease its radius.

All these effects receive immediate interpretation in terms of simple electrostatics and shielding efficiencies.

It is important to remember the limitations inherent in the concept of ionic radii which were mentioned at the beginning of this section, and to retain a flexible attitude in their use. The values in *Table 3.1* refer to six-coordination. For other coordination numbers the interionic repulsive forces experienced by a given ion will be different and this will influence its effective radius. An

Table
Ionic ra
(Numbers in bold face refer to anio

Li	Be	H₃O⁺ 1·14
+1 0·60	+2 0·31	NH₄⁺ 1·48

Na	Mg
+1 0·95	+2 0·65

K	Ca	Sc	Ti	V	Cr	Mn	Fe	Co
+1 1·33	+2 0·99	+3 0·81	+2 0·90 +3 0·76 +4 0·68	+2 0·88 +3 0·74 +4 0·60 +5 0·59	+2 0·84 +3 0·69 +4 0·56 +6 0·52	+2 0·80 +3 0·66 +4 0·54 +7 0·46	+2 0·76 +3 0·64	+2 0· +3 0·6

Rb	Sr	Y	Zr	Nb	Mo	Tc	Ru	Rh
+1 1·48	+2 1·13	+2 ~1·1 +3 0·93	+2 0·93 +4 0·80	+2 ~0·75 +4 0·70 +5 0·70	+4 0·74 +6 0·62	+4 0·6	+4 0·58	+3 ~0

Cs	Ba	La	Hf	Ta	W	Re	Os	Ir
+1 1·69	+2 1·35	+2 ~1·2 +3 1·15	+4 0·81	+2 ~1·0 +4 ~0·7 +5 ᷅0·7	+4 0·74	+4 0·63	+4 0·58	+4 0·

Fr	Ra	Ac
+1 1·76	+2 1·40	+3 1·18

Ce	Pr	Nd	Pm	Sm
+2 1·16 +3 1·11 +4 1·01	+2 1·15 +3 1·09 +4 0·92	+2 1·14 +3 1·08	+3 1·06	+2 1· +3 1·

Th	Pa	U	Np	Pu
+2 ~1·2 +3 1·14 +4 1·01	+2 1·15 +3 1·12 +4 0·98 +5 0·90	+2 1·15 +3 1·11 +4 0·97 +5 0·87	+2 1·14 +3 1·09 +4 0·95 +5 0·88	+2 1· +3 1· +4 0· +5 0·

H⁻ ~1·5
OH⁻ 1·53
SH⁻ 1·99

B	C	N	O	F
+3 0·20	+4 0·15	+5 0·11	+6 0·09	+7 0·07
	−4 2·60	−3 1·71	−2 1·40	−1 1·36

Al	Si	P	S	Cl
+3 0·50	+4 0·41	+5 0·35	+6 0·29	+7 0·26
	−4 2·71	−3 2·12	−2 1·84	−1 1·81

Ni	Cu	Zn	Ga	Ge	As	Se	Br
0·72	+1 0·96	+2 0·74	+1 1·13				
0·62	+2 0·6–0·9		+3 0·62	+2 0·93			
				+4 0·53			
					+5 0·46	+6 0·42	+7 0·39
				−4 2·72	−3 2·22	−2 1·98	−1 1·95

Pd	Ag	Cd	In	Sn	Sb	Te	I
0·86	+1 1·26	+2 0·97	+1 1·32				
	+2 0·7–0·8		+3 0·81	+2 1·12			
						+4 0·89	
				+4 0·71	+5 0·62	+6 0·56	+7 0·50
				−4 2·94	−3 2·45	−2 2·21	−1 2·16

Pt	Au	Hg	Tl	Pb	Bi	Po	At
0·86)	+1 1·37	+2 1·10	+1 1·40				
			+3 0·95	+2 1·20	+3 0·92	+4 1·02	
				+4 0·84	+5 0·74		

Eu	Gd	Tb	Dy	Ho	Er	Tm	Yb	Lu
1·12	+2 ~1·1	+2 ~1·1	+2 ~1·1	+2 ~1·1	+2 ~1·1	+2 ~1·1	+2 1·13	
1·03	+3 1·02	+3 1·00	+3 0·99	+3 0·97	+3 0·96	+3 0·95	+3 0·94	+3 0·93
		+4 0·86						

m	Cm	Bk	Cf	Es	Fm	Md	No	Lr
1·13	+4 0·92							
1·06								
0·92								
0·86								

indication of the magnitude of this effect can be obtained from the approximate expression of the lattice energy:

$$U_L = \frac{N_0 A z_1 z_2 e^2}{r} - \frac{N_0 B e^2}{r^n}$$

Using the condition that $(\partial U_L/\partial r) = 0$ at the equilibrium distance r_0 we have

$$\frac{N_0 A z_1 z_2 e^2}{r_0^2} = \frac{n N_0 B e^2}{r_0^{n+1}}$$

Whence

$$r_0 = \left(\frac{nB}{A z_1 z_2}\right)^{1/(n-1)}$$

It can be seen that the radius depends on the repulsion constant, B, on the Madelung constant A, and on the Born exponent n. If n is given the typical value of 9, and the constant B is considered to be proportional to the number of nearest neighbours, then the change in radius of an ion accompanying a change from the sodium chloride structure to the caesium chloride structure is

$$\frac{r(\text{CsCl})}{r(\text{NaCl})} = \left(\frac{8}{6} \times \frac{1 \cdot 748}{1 \cdot 783}\right)^{\frac{1}{8}} = 1 \cdot 036$$

If $n = 12$ the ratio is $1 \cdot 027$. In other words, the radius of an ion in eightfold coordination is 3 per cent larger than its radius in sixfold coordination. Such changes have been observed experimentally. Similarly, when an ion is in fourfold coordination its radius is some 4 per cent less than its value in sixfold coordination, the differences between the sphalerite and wurtzite Madelung constants being insignificant in this calculation:

$$\left(\frac{4}{6} \times \frac{1 \cdot 746}{1 \cdot 638}\right)^{\frac{1}{8}} \simeq \left(\frac{4}{6} \times \frac{1 \cdot 746}{1 \cdot 641}\right)^{\frac{1}{8}} = 0 \cdot 958$$

Polarization effects may also influence the radius of an ion. As expected, the hydride ion is particularly vulnerable to polarization since the two electrons are bound by the central force field of only one proton. Accordingly, the value obtained for the radius from a series of alkali metal hydrides using the relation

$$r(\text{H}^+) = r_0(\text{M}^+\text{H}^-) - r(\text{M}^+)$$

varies from $1 \cdot 42$ Å (from LiH) to $1 \cdot 54$ Å (from CsH); the value obtained from MgH_2 is 1·30 Å and from the alkaline earth hydrides about 1·35 Å. Normally, however, the effects of polarization on ionic radius do not manifest themselves so acutely.

3.2. Radius Ratio Rules

As cations are generally smaller than anions, the crystal structure is usually determined by the number of anions it is possible to pack around the smaller cation. This can be expressed in terms of the radius ratio, ρ, where

$$\rho = r_{cation}/r_{anion}$$

When the cation is a point charge or is very small, it is only possible to pack two anions around it if anion-cation contact is to be retained:

As the size of the cation increases relative to that of the anion, i.e. as ρ increases, a point is reached when it becomes possible to place three anions around the cation thus increasing the coulomb attractive energy. *Figure 3.1* shows that the critical radius ratio is

$$\rho = \frac{[(2\sqrt{3})/3] - 1}{1} = 0·155$$

As ρ increases beyond this value the cation remains in contact with the three anions around the cation (see *Figure 3.1*). Similarly at $\rho = 0·414$ octahedral coordination just becomes possible and above $\rho = 0·732$, eightfold cubic coordination can occur. The origin of these numbers is clear from *Figure 3.1* and the results are summarized in *Table 3.2*. Values for other coordination numbers such as 5, 7, 9, etc. can easily be derived but are not included because such coordination polyhedra cannot be extended into infinite three-dimensional arrays.

The radius ratios in *Table 3.2* form an invaluable first approximation to the stereochemistry of ionic compounds and a great number of structures can be correlated and interpreted on this criterion. However, it is only one of a series of criteria which determine structure and should not be used in isolation. For example, the data in *Table 3.1* lead to radius ratios of 1·09 for RbF and 1·24 for CsF; these are greater than 1·00 so that twelvefold coordination about a cubo-octahedron might have been expected; but it is not possible to build up a close-packed lattice in which each ion is surrounded by 12 ions of the other kind, hence this coordination number is excluded for this stoichiometry. Again, NH_4F, which has a radius ratio of 1·09 might have been expected to adopt the same structure as RbF considered above, but it crystallizes in the tetrahedral wurtzite structure because of the formation of strong hydrogen bonds between the nitrogen and fluorine atoms.

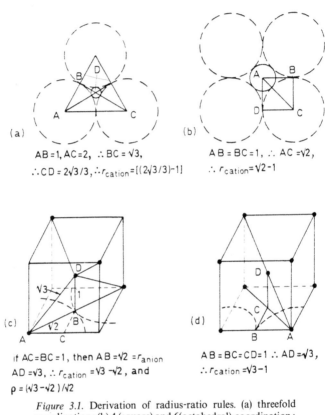

(a)

$$AB = 1, AC = 2, \therefore BC = \sqrt{3},$$
$$\therefore CD = 2\sqrt{3}/3, \therefore r_{cation} = [(2\sqrt{3}/3) - 1]$$

(b)

$$AB = BC = 1, \therefore AC = \sqrt{2},$$
$$\therefore r_{cation} = \sqrt{2} - 1$$

(c)

if $AC = BC = 1$, then $AB = \sqrt{2} = r_{anion}$
$AD = \sqrt{3}, \therefore r_{cation} = \sqrt{3} - \sqrt{2}$, and
$\rho = (\sqrt{3} - \sqrt{2})/\sqrt{2}$

(d)

$$AB = BC = CD = 1 \therefore AD = \sqrt{3},$$
$$\therefore r_{cation} = \sqrt{3} - 1$$

Figure 3.1. Derivation of radius-ratio rules. (a) threefold coordination; (b) 4 (square) and 6(octahedral)-coordination; (c) 4 (tetrahedral)-coordination; (d) 8 (cubic)-coordination

Considerable subtlety is frequently required in the interpretation of radius ratios, particularly near the critical values. This is because (*a*) the actual difference in lattice energy between the two possible structures is frequently very small and may be influenced by polarization effects, (*b*) the actual value of the cation radius changes with

Table 3.2
Influence of radius ratio, ρ, on coordination number

$\rho = r_{cation}/r_{anion}$	Symmetry of anions around cation	Coordination number of cation
1·000–0·732	corners of a cube	8
0·732–0·414	corners of a regular octahedron (or square)	6 (or 4)
0·414–0·225	corners of a regular tetrahedron	4
0·225–0·155	corners of an equilateral triangle	3
0·155–0·000	linear	2

coordination number and this may nullify the apparent gain in lattice energy. Thus Born and Mayer (1932) calculated the lattice energy of several structures as a function of radius ratio and found that the energy differences between the 'stable' and 'unstable' configurations were very small, especially for high coordination numbers. Their results, plotted in *Figure 3.2*, show how vulnerable changes in coordination can be to the presence of slight additional polarization energies. They also show that although there is no further gain in lattice energy in the NaCl-type structure below $\rho = 0.414$, yet the ZnS-type structure does not have a lower energy until about $\rho = 0.32$. This may explain why LiCl and LiBr retain

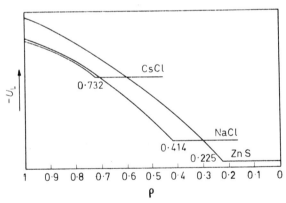

Figure 3.2. Dependence of lattice energy on radius ratio

the CsCl-structure though the fact that LiI ($\rho = 0.278$) also has this structure is surprising; the radius of the octahedral site generated by six iodide ions in contact is $2.16 \times [(\sqrt{2}) - 1] = 0.89$ Å which is

45

50 per cent larger than the normal radius of Li^+. The problem of the transition from octahedral to tetrahedral coordination is a complicated one and a more detailed treatment, including the concept of 'rattling' is given in Dunitz and Orgel's review.[5]

The graphs in *Figure 3.2* were obtained on the assumption that the ionic radii were independent of coordination number. However, as shown in the preceding section the cation and anion radii are expected to increase by some 3 per cent in going from sixfold to eightfold coordination. This means that the internuclear distance in the lattice energy equation (Chapter 2) will increase by this amount thereby *reducing* the lattice energy by 3 per cent. The gain in lattice energy due to the larger Madelung constants is less than 1 per cent so there appears no reason on the purely electrostatic theory why the caesium chloride structure should ever be adopted (and indeed it is relatively uncommon even when radius ratios are compatible with its formation, e.g. RbBr with $\rho = 0.760$ has the NaCl structure at atmospheric pressure). The fact that caesium chloride, bromide, and iodide (and the rubidium halides under pressure) adopt eightfold coordination despite the apparent 2 per cent loss in lattice energy is probably due to the increased London dispersion forces in the higher coordination. As the total lattice energies of these compounds are about 150 kcal/mole the energy changes being considered are only about 3 kcal/mole which is near the limit of accuracy of the simple ionic model and within the range of contribution of polarization and zero-point energies.

As an illustration of the use of radius ratios in understanding the crystal chemistry of compounds, the dioxides of Group IV elements can be considered. The relevant data, taken from *Table 3.1*, are set out below:

CO_2 $\rho = 0.15/1.40 = 0.11$, therefore predict linear coordination from *Table 3.2*, i.e. molecular OCO units as found experimentally;

SiO_2 $\rho = 0.29$, predict 4:2 coordination as found; as each Si must be surrounded by 4 O, each O must be shared between 2 Si thus generating a three-dimensional lattice;

GeO_2 $\rho = 0.38$, predict 4:2 coordination as found (quartz structure);

SnO_2 $\rho = 0.51$, predict 6:3 coordination as found (rutile structure);

PbO_2 $\rho = 0.60$, predict 6:3 coordination as found (rutile structure);

ThO_2 $\rho = 0.73$, predict 8:4 coordination as found (fluorite structure).

3.3 Influence of Polarization on Crystal Structures

The polarizing properties of ions have been discussed in Section 2.7.3 of Chapter 2. The influence of polarization on crystal structures is to distort the three-dimensional arrays in such a way as to give firstly layer lattices and ultimately molecular structures. In this way it can again be seen that polarization effects the transition between ionic and covalent bonding. The effect can be illustrated schematically by considering a planar 4:2 coordination lattice which is the two-dimensional analogue of the 6:3 rutile lattice (p. 55). *Figure 3.3* shows that increasing polarization leads first to a layer lattice analogous to the cadmium iodide lattice (p. 56) and then to a molecular lattice.

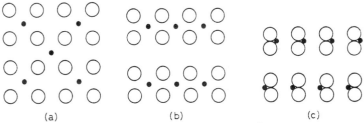

(a)   (b)   (c)

Figure 3.3. Influence of polarization on crystal structure.

It has been seen in earlier sections that polarization depends not only on the size and charge of an ion but also on its coordination number and electronic configuration. An illustration of the increased polarizing power of the d^{10} ion Cu^+ over that of Na^+ (which has the same radius) is given by the cuprous halides, all of which adopt the zinc blende 4:4 structure rather than the sodium chloride 6:6 structure.

Goldschmidt correlated many structures in terms of these trends

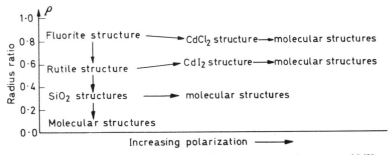

Figure 3.4. Influence of radius ratio and polarization on crystal structure of MX_2 compounds

by means of diagrams such as that in *Figure 3.4*. Some of the structures involved are described in the following sections and a more detailed discussion is given in the bibliography at the end of the chapter.

3.4. Description of Typical MX Structures

Several structure-types occur so frequently that it is convenient to summarize their principal features and interrelationships and to indicate when each is likely to occur. In this section the five principal MX structures will be considered: sodium chloride, caesium chloride, zinc sulphide, zinc oxide, and nickel arsenide. The next section will deal with the five main MX_2 structures: fluorite (CaF_2), rutile (TiO_2), cadmium iodide, cadmium chloride, and lead chlorofluoride. Discussion of more complex binary and ternary oxide structures will be deferred until appropriate places in later chapters.

3.4.1. *Sodium Chloride* (*Rock-salt*)

The sodium chloride lattice consists of two interpenetrating face-centred cubic sub-lattices, each ion being surrounded octahedrally by six ions of the other kind as illustrated in *Figure 3.5*. This diagram illustrates that the unit cell comprises four sodium

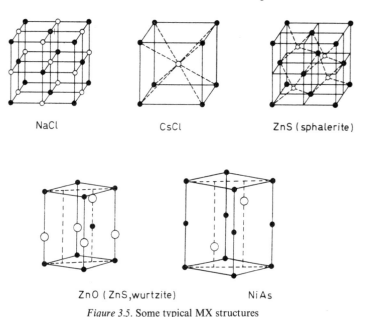

NaCl CsCl ZnS (sphalerite)

ZnO (ZnS,wurtzite) NiAs

Figure 3.5. Some typical MX structures

ions and four chloride ions. In using this and subsequent diagrams it must be remembered that an ion at one of the corners of the cubic unit cell is shared between eight contiguous unit cells and therefore counts only as 1/8th; similarly an ion on a cube edge contributes $\frac{1}{4}$, and an ion at a face centre contributes $\frac{1}{2}$; only when an ion is wholly within the unit cell does it count as a full ion. On this basis the number of solid circles in the NaCl-structure is $(8 \times \frac{1}{8}) + (6 \times \frac{1}{2}) = 4$ and the number of open circles is $(12 \times \frac{1}{4}) + 1 = 4$.

The conditions for the adoption of the NaCl-structure have been fully discussed in the preceding section. It is the most common of the MX structures, more than half of the 400 compounds so far investigated having this structure. It occurs principally among the alkali metal halides and hydrides, the alkaline earth oxides and chalcogenides, the oxides of divalent early first-row transition metals, and the chalcogenides of divalent lanthanide and actinide elements. It also occurs among less ionic compounds such as the nitrides, phosphides, arsenides and bismuthides of the lanthanide and actinide elements, the silver halides (except the iodide) and the tin and lead chalcogenides, however, too great a degree of polarization precludes its formation and usually results in a lower coordination number as discussed in sections 3.4.3 and 3.4.4 below. Many interstitial alloys of appropriate composition such as carbides, nitrides and transition metal hydrides also adopt the sodium structure, as do the following compounds of polyatomic anions which achieve spherical symmetry by rotation in the crystal: KOH, (Na, K, Rb)SH, (Na, K, Rb)SeH, (Na, K, Rb)CN, (Ca, Sr, Ba)NH, and $RbNH_2$.

3.4.2. Caesium Chloride

The caesium chloride structure consists of two interpenetrating simple cubic lattices so that each ion is at the body-centre of a cube of eight ions of the other type as illustrated in *Figure 3.5*. The unit cell contains one CsCl unit. This structure is rarely adopted by ionic compounds even when the radius ratio appears favourable, for reasons discussed in Section 3.3 above, and in ionic compounds it only occurs with univalent ions. It is confined to:

(a) the chlorides, bromides and iodides of the largest cations (caesium, thallium(I) and ammonium) though the ammonium halides revert to the sodium chloride structure above 184°, 138°, and −18° respectively;

(b) polyatomic anions with caesium and thallium: Cs(CN, SH, SeH, NH_2) and TlCN;

49

E

(c) intermetallic compounds such as β-brass, CuZn; one component of these alloys is usually Li, Cu, Ag, Au, Tl; Be, Mg, Zn, Cd, (Hg); or Al. It is also interesting that ThTe ($\rho = 0.46$) has the caesium chloride structure rather than the sodium chloride structure which is adopted by ThS ($\rho = 0.55$) and ThSe ($\rho = 0.51$).

3.4.3. Cubic Zinc Sulphide (Zinc blende or Sphalerite)

The cubic zinc sulphide structure has fourfold coordination as shown in *Figure 3.5* and is closely related both to the sodium chloride structure and the zinc oxide structure (p. 51). A face-centred cubic array of N lattice points generates N octahedral interstitial sites and $2N$ tetrahedral sites. If all the octahedral sites are filled with a second type of ion the sodium chloride structure results; if half the tetrahedral sites are filled in an ordered way by a second type of ion then the zinc sulphide structure results; (if all the tetrahedral sites are filled the fluorite structure, p. 54, is formed). The tetrahedral coordination is favoured by:

(a) an ionic radius ratio below 0·414;
(b) cations with high polarizing power (e.g. Cu^+, Ag^+; Be^{2+}, Zn^{2+}, Cd^{2+}, Hg^{2+}; Al^{3+}, Ga^{3+}, In^{3+}) and anions which are readily polarizable (e.g. I^-; S^{2-}, Se^{2-}, Te^{2-}; P^{3-}, As^{3-}, Sb^{3-});
(c) factors which tend to give tetrahedral covalent bonds (e.g. in BN, SiC) or hydrogen bonds (e.g. in NH_4F).

Clearly it is unrealistic to distinguish between purely ionic and purely covalent compounds in this structure and the charges on the ions above are merely a formal indication of their valency. About 30 MX compounds have the zinc blende structure:

Cu(F, Cl, Br, I), AgI; Be(S, Se, Te), Zn(S, Se, Te), Cd(S, Te), Hg(S, Se, Te), Mn(S, Se); B(N, P, As), Al(P, As, Sb), Ga(P, As, Sb), In(P, As, Sb); SiC.

The extent to which polarization in these structures has enforced deviations from the predictions of simple ionic radius ratio theory is seen from the fact that of the halides and chalcogenides listed above only the chalcogenides of beryllium and zinc, and manganese selenide have formal values of ρ less than 0·414.

It is not essential for exactly half the terahedral sites (i.e. N sites) to be filled. For example, if only $\frac{2}{3}$ N sites are occupied in a regular way the structures of Ga_2S_3, Ga_2Se_3, Ga_2Te_3, and In_2Te_3 are obtained. Anticipating Section 5.4, these formulae can be written as $\square Ga_2S_3$ etc. and, counting the blanks as atoms, all the compounds, like the regular zinc blende compounds, have an average of four valency electrons per atom. Likewise in Ag_2HgI_4 threequarters of the N available cation sites are occupied ($\square Ag_2HgI_4$). Another variation of the zinc blende structure occurs in Sn_2O where only $\frac{1}{2}N$ of the anion sites are occupied.

3.4.4. Zinc Oxide (Hexagonal Zinc Sulphide or Wurtzite)

This tetrahedrally coordinated structure is illustrated in *Figure 3.5*. It differs from the cubic zinc sulphide structure only in the stacking of the tetrahedra : if these are stacked in close-packed hexagonal array with the tetrahedral edges of alternate layers rotated through 180° about the c-axis then the ZnO structure results; if all the tetrahedra are parallel to each other the layers repeat in close-packed cubic array and the ZnS structure results. Because of the close similarity of the two structures very similar conditions obtain for their occurrence and indeed several compounds can exist in both forms. As the difference in structure is one of stacking patterns the possibility of mixed stacking sequences arises and the complex structures which are observed with some modifications of SiC and ZnS stem from this cause. For example if the sequence of layers along a body diagonal in the face-centred cubic unit cell is designated abc, abc, abc, ... and the sequence along the c-axis of the hexagonal cell as ab, ab, ab, ... then the various forms of silicon carbides have either of these simple repeat patterns or more complex sequences such as abac, abac, abac, ... or abcacb, abcacb ... or acabcbabcacbcab, ... or even more intricate arrays with a repeat pattern after 21 or 33 layers.

The compounds which crystallize in the simple ZnO structure are : Cu(H, Cl, Br, I), AgI; BeO, MgTe, Zn(O, S, Se, Te), Cd(S, Se), Mn(S, Se, Te); (Al, Ga, In, Nb, Ta)N; SiC; NH_4F. Again it can be seen that radius ratio is not a dominant factor for the halides and chalcogenides. Comparison of this list with that for ZnS structure reveals that the ZnO structure is, in a sense, intermediate between the sodium chloride and zinc sulphide structures. As polarization and covalency increase the NaCl-structure gives way first to the ZnO-structure and then to the ZnS-structure. No compound of the readily ionizable alkali metals or alkaline earth metals crystallizes with fourfold coordination. With magnesium, which has a higher ionization energy (*Table 2.1*) and a measurable polarizing power the oxide, sulphide and selenide are NaCl-type; the more readily polarized telluride ion (*Table 2.10*) permits the ZnO-type but no compound of magnesium adopts the ZnS-structure. By contrast zinc, which has a similar radius to magnesium (*Table 3.1*) but is harder to ionize and is more strongly polarizing, crystallizes none of the analogous compounds in the NaCl-structure; the oxide itself crystallizes as ZnO-type, the sulphide as both ZnO- and ZnS-type, whereas the more polarizable selenide and telluride adopt only the ZnS-structure. Similarly, nitrides are less polarizable than phosphides and accordingly crystallize as ZnO-type whereas the phosphides, arsenides and antimonides have the ZnS-structure. Finally it is significant that, in the sequence of isoelectronic compounds NaF, MgO, AlN, SiC, the first two adopt the NaCl structure, the third has the ZnO structure whereas the last can be either ZnO or ZnS-type; if, on the other hand the same cations are used but a more readily polarizable isoelectronic sequence of anions is chosen, as in NaI, MgTe, AlSb, then only the first is NaCl-type; the second has already adopted the ZnO-type whereas AlSb adopts the ZnS-structure exclusively.

The reason why the more ionic 4-coordinate compounds tend to adopt the hexagonal ZnO structure is probably related to the fact that this structure has a marginally (0·2 per cent) higher Madelung constant (*Table 2.3*) and should also have the larger entropy since there is less intrinsic order in a repeat pattern ab, ab than in the pattern abc, abc.

3.4.5. Nickel Arsenide

The four structure types so far described have two features in common:

(*a*) The M sites and the X sites have the same coordination number and symmetry;

(*b*) The M lattice and the X lattice are entirely equivalent in the structure.

These features do not persist with nickel arsenide. *Figure 3.6* shows

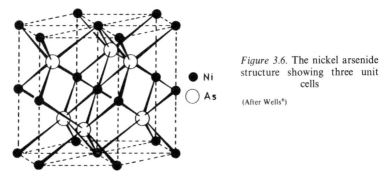

● Ni

○ As

Figure 3.6. The nickel arsenide structure showing three unit cells

(After Wells[6])

that the nickel atoms (M = ●) have eightfold coordination, being surrounded octahedrally by the six arsenic atoms shown (As = ○)

and by two additional nickel atoms which are coplanar with four of the arsenics; by contrast the arsenic atoms are surrounded by a trigonal prism of nickels and are themselves hexagonal-close-packed as in ZnO. Normally the more metallic component of the compound occupies the site of higher coordination. *Figure 3.6* encompasses three unit cells to emphasize the coordination of the nickel atom; the true unit cell, containing two formula weights, is shown in *Figure 3.5* which is identical with the front right hand segment of *Figure 3.6*. A significant feature of the structure is the close approach of the M atoms in chains along the c (vertical) axis—these vertical stacks of trigonal prisms allow the M atoms much closer approach than in the sodium chloride structure. In this sense the structure can be regarded as a transition between the ionic sodium-chloride structure and metallic structures. Indeed, if the NiAs structure were purely ionic it would never be stable with respect to the sodium chloride lattice because it has an appreciably lower Madelung constant. Thus, NiAs itself has a Madelung constant of 1·693 and this varies with the c/a ratio in the crystal between 1·666 ($c/a = 1·3$) and 1·727 ($c/a = 1·9$) with a maximum at 1·733 ($c/a = 1·77$).[1] All these values fall below the sodium-chloride value of 1·748.

The nickel arsenide structure forms (with the caesium chloride structure) the second most prevalent MX structural type after sodium chloride. It is peculiar to compounds of the transition elements (especially of the first row) with the chalcogens, arsenic, antimony and bismuth, and to a lesser extent tin. Compounds adopting this structure are: ScTe, Ti(S, Se, Te), V(S, Se, Te, P), Cr(S, Se, Te, Sb), Mn(Te, As, Sb, Bi), Fe(S, Se, Te, Sb, Sn), Co(S, Se, Te, Sb), Ni(S, Se, Te, As, Sb, Sn), Pd(Te, Sb, Sn), Pt(Sb, Bi, Sn), Rh(Te, Bi, Sn) and isolated compounds such as CuSn, AuSn, IrTe, IrSb, NbS and ZrTe. Vanadium arsenide and the phosphides and arsenides of Cr, Mn, Fe and Co have a distorted nickel arsenide (MnP) structure. The pattern of elements is clear and can be contrasted with the sodium-chloride structure adopted by the monoxides of the first row transition elements. It is evident that radius ratio is not the dominant criterion favouring this structure but rather the tendency towards higher coordination and metallic bonding as evidenced by the compounds' opacity, high electrical conductivity and ability to exist over quite wide composition ranges. The trend is thus in the opposite direction to those transitions from ionic bonding which lead to covalency, for these tend to lower the coordination number to four, as in the zinc oxide and zinc sulphide structures.

[1] Zemann, J., *Acta Cryst.*, **11** (1958) 55

The five structure types so far considered account for over 80 per cent of all compounds with the stoichiometry MX, and half of the remaining compounds have structures which can be regarded as distortions of these five main types. Few of the remaining compounds can be considered ionic and many are purely molecular, e.g. HCl, H_2O_2, N_4S_4, B_4Cl_4. They will therefore not be considered further.

3.5. Description of Typical MX_2 Structures

The same principles apply to these compounds as to those of MX stoichiometry just considered. The structures of compounds with weakly polarizing inert-gas-configuration ions tend to be governed by the radius rules (*Table 3.2*) whereas transition-metal compounds and those with d^{10} cations reflect the influence of increasing polarization and covalency by adopting layer-lattice structures. MX_2 stoichiometry can also be achieved by the presence of diatomic anions as in CaC_2 or KCN though these are best considered as distorted MX structures. The structures of about 400 MX_2 compounds have been determined and over 80 per cent of these fall into one of five main structural types or distortions of these. The structures are fluorite (CaF_2), rutile (TiO_2), CdI_2, $CdCl_2$, and PbClF and these will be discussed in the following sections. Purely molecular structures such as CO_2 or N_2H_4 will not be considered.

3.5.1. Calcium Fluoride (Fluorite)

The fluorite structure consists of a close-packed cubic array of cations in which all the tetrahedral sites are occupied by anions as

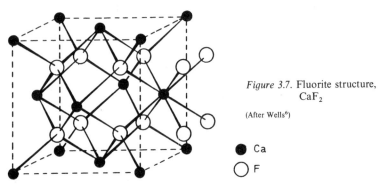

Figure 3.7. Fluorite structure, CaF_2

(After Wells[6])

● Ca
○ F

illustrated in *Figure 3.7*. The relation to zinc blende structure (*Figure 3.5*) in which only half the tetrahedral sites are occupied is obvious. Each anion is surrounded tetrahedrally by cations and each cation is surrounded by eight anions at the corners of a cube. The structure is therefore expected for ionic MX$_2$ compounds with a radius ratio above 0·73. It occurs in four main types of compound:

(a) fluorides of large divalent cations (Ca, Sr, Ba, Ra; Cd, Hg; Pb), and in SrCl$_2$, BaCl$_2$ and the dihydrides of many lanthanide elements; the divalent cation can also be substituted for the stoichiometric equivalent of pairs or triplets of cations, e.g. NaYF$_4$, KLaF$_4$, Na$_2$ThF$_6$, K$_2$UF$_6$, etc.;

(b) the oxides of large quadrivalent cations (Zr, Hf; Ce, Pr, Tb; Po; Th, Pa, U, Np, Pu, Am) and the oxyfluorides, MOF, of large ter-valent cations (Y; La, Ce, Pr, Nd, Sm, Ho; Ac, Pu); [note that with Zr^{4+} and Hf^{4+} the radius ratio falls to 0·67 and with Y^{3+} and Am^{4+} it falls as far as 0·57 whilst still retaining the fluorite structure; this reflects the fact that the Madelung constant for the eight-coordinate fluorite structure (5·039) is appreciably higher than for the six-coordinate rutile structure to be discussed below ($A = 4·816$) thus prolonging its range of existence];

(c) the oxides and chalcogenides of the alkali metals M$_2$X in which the occupation of the cation and anion sites in *Figure 3.7* is reversed (antifluorite structure): Li$_2$(NH, O, S, Se, Te); Na$_2$(O, S, Se, Te); K$_2$(O, S, Se, Te), Rb$_2$(O, S);

(d) a number of intermetallic and miscellaneous compounds such as Au(Al$_2$, Ga$_2$, In$_2$, Sb$_2$); Pt(Al$_2$, Ga$_2$, In$_2$, Sn$_2$); (Bi, Ge, Sn, Pb)Mg$_2$; (Co, Ni)Si$_2$; (Ir$_2$, Rh$_2$)P; Be$_2$(B, C) and IrSn$_2$.

3.5.2. *Rutile*, TiO$_2$ (*or Cassiterite*, SnO$_2$)

When the radius ratio falls below 0·7, sixfold coordination of the anions about the cations becomes prevalent and for non-polarizable anions such as fluoride and oxide the most common structure adopted is the tetragonal rutile structure shown in *Figure 3.8*;

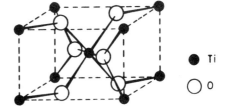

Figure 3.8. Rutile structure, TiO$_2$

(After Wells[6])

● Ti

◯ O

in this, each cation is surrounded octahedrally by six anions and each anion has three coplanar cationic nearest neighbours at the corners of an almost equilateral triangle.

The only divalent metal fluorides having cations with the appropriate radius are those of Cr, Mn, Fe, Co, Ni, Cu, Zn, and Pd; all
— of these have the rutile structure except CrF_2 and CuF_2 which adopt a distorted rutile structure as a result of ligand field effects on the d^4 and d^9 configurations respectively. Oxides of quadrivalent metals having the appropriate cation radius also crystallize in the rutile structure, e.g. those of Ti, Nb, Ta; Cr, Mo, W; Mn; Ru, Os; Ir; Ge, Sn, Pb; Te.

As with the fluorite structure it is possible to substitute stoichiometrically equivalent combinations of ions of appropriate size, e.g. the two M^{4+} cations in the unit cell can be replaced by combinations of cations having an average valency of four: $AlSbO_4$, $GaSbO_4$; $Cr(Nb, Ta, Sb)O_4$; $Fe(Nb, Ta, Sb)O_4$; $Rh(V, Nb, Ta, Sb)O_4$.

When the radius ratio of the divalent metal fluoride or quadrivalent metal oxide falls below 0·4 tetrahedral coordination would be expected, as discussed on p. 43. Such structures are rather uncommon and are usually complex. They occur in the various forms of SiO_2 and in SiS_2, soluble GeO_2, GeS_2, BeF_2, $Be(OH)_2$, $BeCl_2$, $ZnBr_2$ and HgI_2. More frequently, with smaller or more highly polarizing cations in combination with anions which are more polarizable then fluoride and oxide, the structures adopt one of several possible layer lattice types which will now be considered.

3.5.3. Cadmium Iodide Structure

Cadmium iodide has a layer lattice structure in which each cadmium is coordinated octahedrally by six iodide ions but each iodide

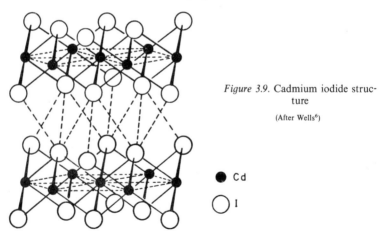

Figure 3.9. Cadmium iodide structure

(After Wells[6])

● Cd

○ I

is coordinated by three cadmiums on one side only, as shown in *Figure 3.9*. The iodide ions (I = ◯) are in hexagonal close packing and half the octahedral interstices are occupied by cadmium ions. Detailed inspection of this structure reveals that it is closely related to the nickel arsenide structure (*Figures 3.5* and *3.6*) in which all the octahedrally coordinated interstices in the hexagonally close-packed arsenic lattice are occupied by nickel atoms. This becomes clear when the two unit cells are compared (*Figure 3.10*).

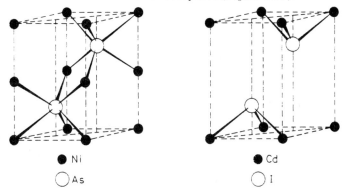

● Ni   ● Cd

◯ As   ◯ I

Figure 3.10. Relation between the structures of NiAs and CdI$_2$. NiAs has two moles per unit cell (Ni$_2$As$_2$) whereas CdI$_2$ has only one
(After Wells[6])

The cadium iodide structure is the next most prevalent MX$_2$ structure after fluorite and occurs predominantly in those compounds where marked polarization effects are to be expected:

(a) the iodides of moderately polarizing cations, the bromides and iodides of d^{10} and transition element cations and magnesium, and even some chlorides of more highly polarizing cations, e.g. Ti^{2+} and V^{2+}: (Ca, Cd, Ge, Pb, Th, Tm, Yb)I$_2$; Mg(Br$_2$, I$_2$); Mn(Br$_2$, I$_2$); Fe(Br$_2$, I$_2$); Co(Br$_2$, I$_2$); Ti(Cl$_2$, Br$_2$, I$_2$); V(Cl$_2$, Br$_2$, I$_2$);

(b) the hydroxides of many divalent cations of even moderate polarizing power, since the OH$^-$ ion has a permanent dipole and is thus able to induce the layer lattice formation, e.g. the dihydroxides of Mg, Ca, Mn, Fe, Co, Ni;

(c) the dichalcogenides (but not the less-polarizable oxides) of many quadrivalent metals, e.g. the disulphides, diselenides and ditellurides of Ti, Zr, and Pt; the disulphides and diselenides of Hf and Sn; TaS$_2$; and (Co, Ni, Pd, Rh, Ir, Si)Te$_2$.

The only substances falling outside this classification which adopt the cadmium iodide structure are a few hydroxide halides such as

$Co(OH)_{1.5}Br_{0.5}$, $Co(OH)_{1.5}Cl_{0.5}$, and $Ni(OH)_{1.5}Cl_{0.5}$; a few other intermediate compounds such as SnSSe, BiTeBr, and BiTeI; and the anti-cadmium iodide structures of Ag_2F and W_2C.

3.5.4. Cadmium Chloride Structure

If the anion lattice in MX_2 is cubic-close-packed and half the octahedral interstices are occupied by cations, then the cadmium chloride structure illustrated in *Figure 3.11* results. It is thus related

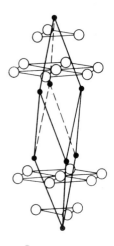

Figure 3.11. The rhombohedral unit cell of $CdCl_2$ containing one mole

The cations (●) are in cubic close packing and are vertically above the anions (○) in the next but one adjacent layer

(From Wyckoff[2], by courtesy of Interscience Publishers Ltd.)

to the cadmium iodide structure in much the same way as the cubic zinc blende is related to the hexagonal zinc oxide structure (p. 51). In cadmium iodide the layers are superimposed so that the cations of one layer are directly above the cations in the next layer whereas in the cadmium chloride structure each cation is directly above (or below) an anion in the next but one layer.

Just as the zinc oxide structure was in a sense intermediate between the sodium chloride and zinc blende structures, so the cadmium chloride structure is intermediate between the fluorite and rutile structures on the one hand, and the cadmium iodide structure on the other. In other words, it occurs when the extent of polarization is not so pronounced as in the compounds which adopt the cadmium iodide structure. The compounds known to adopt the cadmium chloride structure are thus the chlorides (and occasionally the bromides and iodides) of moderately strongly polarizing divalent cations and the sulphides (but not the selenides or tellurides) of moderately polarizing quadrivalent cations:

$MgCl_2$; $MnCl_2$, $FeCl_2$, $CoCl_2$; $Ni(Cl_2, Br_2, I_2)$;

$Zn(Cl_2, Br_2, I_2)$; $Cd(Cl_2, Br_2)$; PbI_2; NbS_2, TaS_2.

Occasionally mixed hydroxide chlorides also occur in this structure, e.g. $Mg(OH)Cl$, $Ni(OH)Cl$, $Cd(OH)_{1.25}Cl_{0.75}$, and $Cd(OH)_{1.25}Br_{0.75}$. Caesium oxide, Cs_2O, has the anti-cadmium chloride structure.

As with the zinc blende-zinc oxide structures so with the cadmium chloride-cadmium iodide structures it is possible to have complex sequences of cubic and hexagonal layers. Thus, instead of anion layer sequences abc, abc ... or ab, ab ..., sequences such as abac, abac ... and progressively more complex unit cells are possible. This accounts for the many crystallographic modifications of compounds such as $NiBr_2$, $CdBr_2$, CdI_2, PbI_2, TaS_2 and Tl_2S.

The only other widely adopted MX_2 layer lattice is the lead chlorofluoride structure described in the next section.

3.5.5. Lead Chlorofluoride, PbClF

Lead chlorofluoride has a layered tetragonal structure and this structure is adopted by about 50 other compounds, i.e. about as

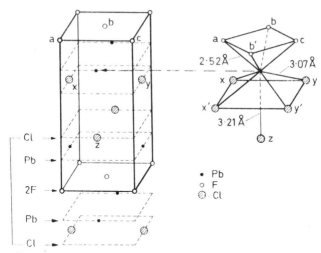

Figure 3.12. Lead chlorofluoride tetragonal unit cell showing sequence of layers and coordination around the lead atom

many as have the cadmium iodide structure. The unit cell, which contains two moles, is shown in *Figure 3.12*. It consists of plane sheets of fluoride ions sandwiched between planar layers of chloride ions, the lead layers being between the fluorides and chlorides so that the layer sequence is ClPbFPbCl, ClPbFPbCl, ... There are twice as many ions in the fluoride layer as in the chloride or lead layers so the stoichiometry is PbClF. *Figure 3.12* also shows that each lead ion is surrounded by four fluoride ions at 2·52 Å and by five chloride ions (four at 3·07 Å and one from an adjacent layer at 3·21 Å). It is significant that these distances are precisely the values calculated from the ionic radii in *Table 3.1* if allowance is made for a 5 per cent expansion of Pb^{2+} on going from 6- to 8-coordination. Indeed the symmetry of the fluorides around the lead is just that found in the fluorite modification of PbF_2 (see *Figure 3.7*) and the adoption of a layer lattice structure reflects the attempt to accommodate two anions of considerably different size rather than any tendency towards polarization with its consequent diminution in bond distances.

As expected from the observations in the preceding paragraph the lead chlorofluoride structure is expected for compounds of weakly or moderately polarizing cations with two anions of differing size which have low or moderate polarizabilities. Three typical situations arise:

(a) M is a large bivalent cation and the anions are either halide ions or the hydride ion: CaH(Cl, Br, I), SrH(Cl, Br, I), BaH(Cl, Br, I); PbF(Cl, Br);

(b) M is a large tervalent cation, one of the anions is the oxide ion and the other is a halide ion (but not F^-, since this has a radius close to that of O^{2-}, the only exception being BiOF), e.g. MOCl where M^{3+} is Y; La, Ce, Pr, Nd, Sm, Eu, Gd, Tb, Dy, Ho, Er; Bi; Ac, U, Am; MOBr where M^{3+} is La, Nd, Bi, Pu, Am; MOI where M^{3+} is Y, La, Sm, Tm, Bi, Pu.

(c) M is a large quadrivalent cation and the anions are oxide and a chalcogenide, e.g. ThO(S, Se, Te); PaOS; UO(S, Se), NpOS, PuOS.

The only example of the lead chlorofluoride structure arising in a compound where the two anions have identical radii is uranium ditelluride, though bismuth oxyfluoride is also unusual as mentioned above. Numerous other MXY and MX_2 compounds have structures which can be considered as distortions of the PbClF structure.

References for Further Reading

1. Pauling, L., *Nature of the Chemical Bond* (3rd edn), Cornell University Press, 1960

REFERENCES

2. Wyckoff, R. W. G., *Crystal Structures*, Vol. 1 (2nd edn), Interscience, New York, 1963
3. Stillwell, C. W., *Crystal Chemistry*, McGraw-Hill, New York, 1938
4. Evans, R. C., *An Introduction to Crystal Chemistry* (2nd edn), Cambridge University Press, 1964
5. Dunitz, J. D. and Orgel, L. E., 'Stereochemistry of Ionic Solids', *Adv. inorg. Chem. Radiochem.*, 2 (1960) 1–60
6. Wells, A. F., *Structural Inorganic Chemistry* (3rd edn), Oxford University Press, 1962
7. Goldschmidt, V. M., 'Crystal Structure and Chemical Constitution', *Trans. Faraday Soc.*, 25 (1929) 253–283
8. Parthé, E., *Crystal Chemistry of Tetrahedral Structures*, Gordon and Breach, New York, 1964

4

LATTICE DEFECTS

THE theory of ionic crystals which has been developed in the preceding two chapters can be thought of as a theory of ideal crystals. In an ideal crystal, each ion is situated on the appropriate lattice site and each lattice site is occupied by the appropriate ion. Such a crystal will have an accurately stoichiometric formula but can only be in true thermodynamic equilibrium at the absolute zero since it has an effectively zero entropy. At temperatures above $0°K$ all crystals must deviate to some extent from the perfect state due to the appearance of lattice defects. Just as many important properties of gases (such as the Joule–Thomson effect, and the fact that gases can be condensed into liquids) derive from their imperfections, so do many of the properties of real crystals arise from their imperfections (for example, their ionic conduction, diffusion, and ability to react chemically).

In the general treatment of lattice defects seven or eight types of primary imperfections are recognized:[1]

(i) Phonons, i.e. 'particles' associated with unit quantum excitation of one of the modes of elastic vibration of the ideal crystal;
(ii) electrons and positive holes;
(iii) excitons, i.e. excited electrons accompanied by and bound to their holes; excitons arise as the first and other low excited non-conducting states of insulators;
(iv) vacant lattice sites and interstitial atoms or ions;
(v) impurity atoms in either interstitial or substitutional positions;
(vi) dislocations;
(vii) stacking faults.

We shall be dealing principally with types (iv) and (v) which may be called equilibrium atomic defects. It is these defects which are most closely related to the chemical properties of crystals. Dislocations are also imperfections in atomic arrangement but are of a non-equilibrium nature. They are more complex and less completely

---

[1] Seitz, F. 'Imperfections in Nearly Perfect Crystals: A Synthesis', pp. 3–76 in ref. 1 at end of Chapter.

understood than the other types of primary imperfections but are of great importance in theories of crystal growth and plastic deformation. In some classifications of defects the surface of the crystal itself is also taken to be a defect because the regular infinite array of the perfect crystal is abruptly terminated; this leaves many atoms or ions in special positions both energetically and structually and these surface states have, a profound influence on the behaviour of the system.

In addition to the seven or eight primary imperfections there are three types of transient imperfections:

(i) electromagnetic quanta (from radiofrequencies to γ-rays);
(ii) charged radiations such as fast positive and negative ions, e.g. α- and β-particles;
(iii) uncharged radiations, e.g. neutrons.

The importance of recognizing all these types of imperfections even though we shall be concentrating on only two of the main classes is that imperfections interact among themselves to create fresh defects, so that a full understanding of any one class is not possible without some knowledge of the others. For example, vacant lattice sites may be formed by thermal vibration (phonons), by the presence of impurity atoms, by the interaction of the lattice with its dislocations, or by the action of charged or uncharged radiations. Radioactive recoil within a crystal may also result in defect formation. The vacant lattice sites can trap electrons, holes or excitons, or absorb light quanta, and so on. Finally, in the general classification of defects, there are certain specialized imperfections such as stacking faults, spin waves etc., which may confer individual properties (e.g. ferromagnetism) on the crystal.

In the following treatment the discussion will be restricted almost entirely to equilibrium atomic defects and in particular to type (iv) above, that is to imperfections involving vacant lattice sites and interstitial ions. Such defects fall into two categories:

(i) those which are *inherent* in the thermodynamics of the solid state and which must occur in all crystals;
(ii) those which are *specific* to the particular crystalline compound considered.

It will be convenient to concentrate initially on the first category. There are two types of inherent thermodynamic defect: Schottky defects[1] and Frenkel defects.[2] The theory of these defects will be

[1] Schottky, W. and Wagner, C., Z. phys. Chem., **11B** (1930) 163; Schottky, W., Z. phys. Chem., **29B** (1935) 353
[2] Frenkel, I., Z. Phys., **35** (1926) 652

discussed in the next section and experimental evidence for their existence will be presented in Section 4.2. Inherent defects are sometimes referred to as native imperfections.

4.1. Inherent Thermodynamic Defects

A Schottky defect consists of a vacant cation lattice site and a vacant anion lattice site as shown in *Figure 4.1*. Schottky defects

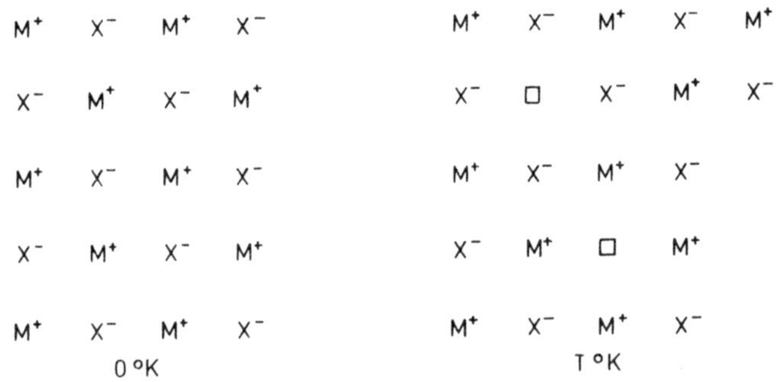

$$
\begin{array}{cccc}
M^+ & X^- & M^+ & X^- \\
X^- & M^+ & X^- & M^+ \\
M^+ & X^- & M^+ & X^- \\
X^- & M^+ & X^- & M^+ \\
M^+ & X^- & M^+ & X^-
\end{array}
\qquad
\begin{array}{ccccc}
M^+ & X^- & M^+ & X^- & M^+ \\
X^- & \square & X^- & M^+ & X^- \\
M^+ & X^- & M^+ & X^- & \\
X^- & M^+ & \square & M^+ & \\
M^+ & X^- & M^+ & X^- &
\end{array}
$$

0 °K   T °K

Figure 4.1. Formation of a Schottky defect in a crystal MX. The ideal crystal at the absolute zero is completely regular, above that temperature there are equal numbers of vacant sites in the cation and anion sublattices

arise effectively by ions leaving their normal lattice positions and building on to the surface of the crystal. In the simple case of a stoichiometric compound MX, such vacant sites must occur equally in the cation and anion sublattices to preserve overall electrical neutrality at the surface. If the composition is MX_2 then the Schottky defect comprises a vacant cation site and two vacant anion sites.

A Frenkel defect consists of an interstitial ion and a vacant lattice site. Frenkel defects are formed by ions leaving their normal lattice sites to take up interstitial positions, as illustrated in *Figure 4.2*. Because ionic size is important, the occurrence of Frenkel defects is frequently limited to the sublattice of the smaller ion, usually the cation; it does not affect both the cation and the anion sublattices equally as do Schottky defects.

It may at first seem surprising that all crystals in thermodynamic equilibrium are subject to defects in this way. The defects arise from the spontaneous tendency of all systems to increase their entropy or degree of disorder. A crystal is a highly ordered array of ions of low entropy; complete randomization of these ions would give a fluid with a much larger entropy but this randomization is opposed by the fact that the formation of defects requires energy, in the same way that fusion or vaporization requires energy. At any temperature there will be a balance between these two opposing tendencies and at equilibrium the degree of disorder (the number of defects) will be such as to minimize the free energy of the crystal. To calculate the

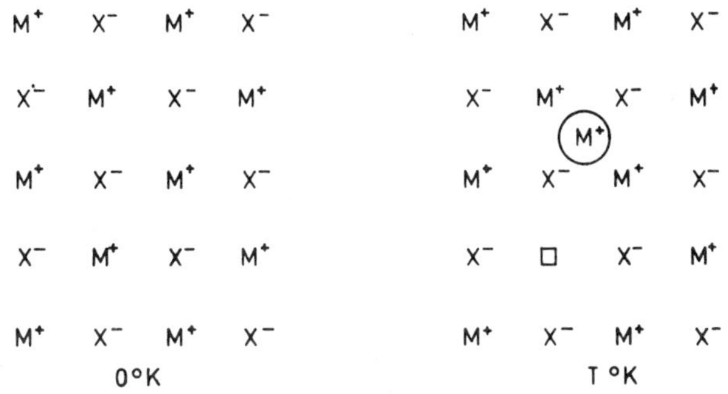

M$^+$	X$^-$	M$^+$	X$^-$	M$^+$	X$^-$	M$^+$	X$^-$
X$^-$	M$^+$	X$^-$	M$^+$	X$^-$	M$^+$	X$^-$	M$^+$
M$^+$	X$^-$	M$^+$	X$^-$	M$^+$	X$^-$	M$^+$	X$^-$
X$^-$	M$^+$	X$^-$	M$^+$	X$^-$	□	X$^-$	M$^+$
M$^+$	X$^-$	M$^+$	X$^-$	M$^+$	X$^-$	M$^+$	X$^-$

0°K   T °K

Figure 4.2. Formation of a Frenkel defect. The ideally regular crystal at the absolute zero is disordered by having interstitial ions and an equivalent number of vacant sites in one of the sublattices

number of defects present in a structure at any temperature it is therefore necessary to find an expression for the free energy of the crystal and to minimize this with respect to the number of defects. This will be done in the next two sections.

4.1.1. *Equilibrium Concentration of Schottky Defects*

It is convenient initially to consider the system at constant volume. Then the change in Helmholz free energy (ΔA) is related to changes in the internal energy (ΔU) and entropy (ΔS) by the expression:

$$\Delta A = \Delta U - T\Delta S \qquad (1)$$

The energy required to form defects increases the internal energy ΔU and hence also the free energy ΔA, but the concomitant increase in entropy acts in the opposite direction and therefore lowers the free energy. To calculate the number of Schottky defects in thermodynamic equilibrium at a given temperature explicit expressions for ΔU and ΔS (and hence ΔA) in terms of the number of defects must be obtained; ΔA is then minimized by differentiating with respect to the number of defects and equating to zero, i.e. $(\partial \Delta A / \partial n_s)_{T,V} = 0$ at equilibrium.

Let n_s be the number of Schottky defects per cm^3 at T°K, (that is, there are n_s vacant cation sites and n_s vacant anion sites per cm^3);

65

F

let N be the number of ion pairs ideally present per cm^3 (that is, there are N possible cation sites and N possible anion sites per cm^3); and let w_s be the work required to remove one cation and one anion from the bulk of the crystal to the surface (that is, w_s is the energy required to form one Schottky defect). Then $n_s w_s$ is the energy to form n_s defects and this equals the increase in internal energy per cm^3:

$$\Delta U = n_s w_s \tag{2}$$

The simultaneous increase in entropy is obtained from the Boltzmann relation between entropy and probability (P):

$$\Delta S = k \ln P \tag{3}$$

where k is the Boltzmann constant. The probability or number of different ways in which n_s vacant cation sites and $(N - n_s)$ occupied cation sites can be distributed on N possible cation lattice sites is

$$p = N!/[(N - n_s)! \, n_s!] \tag{4}$$

This may be seen as follows: the total number of ways of putting N different objects on N sites is $N!$ since there are N choices as to where to put the first object, $(N - 1)$ choices for the second, $(N - 2)$ choices for the third, and so on. However, in the present problem there are not N different types of object but only two: cations and vacancies. The $(N - n_s)$ occupied sites can be occupied in $(N - n_s)!$ ways which are identical and the n_s vacant sites have $n_s!$ identical permutations so that the number of distinct ways of putting $(N - n_s)$ cations and n_s vacancies on N sites is as given by equation (4). The same argument applies to the anion lattice. The total distinct number of ways of simultaneously arranging n_s cation vacancies and n_s anion vacancies on the lattice will be the product of their separate probabilities so that $P = p^2$.

$$\Delta S = k \ln P = k \ln p^2 = 2k \ln p$$

Hence

$$\Delta S = 2k \ln \frac{N!}{(N - n_s)! \, n_s!} \tag{5}$$

This is in fact the standard equation for the entropy of mixing of two species and occurs, for example, in the statistical mechanical theory of binary liquid mixtures. We now have both ΔU and ΔS as functions of n_s but it is not possible to differentiate the log of a factorial directly. To proceed, we use Stirling's Approximation:

$$\ln x! \simeq x \ln x - x + \tfrac{1}{2} \ln (2\pi x)$$

When x is sufficiently large† the last two terms can be neglected, giving the super-Stirling Approximation:

$$\ln x! \simeq x \ln x \qquad (6)$$

Applying this to equation (5):

$$\Delta S = 2k[N \ln N - (N - n_s) \ln (N - n_s) - n_s \ln n_s] \qquad (7)$$

Combining equations (1), (2) and (7)

$$\Delta A = n_s w_s - 2kT[N \ln N - (N - n_s) \ln (N - n_s) - n_s \ln n_s]$$

For equilibrium $(\partial \Delta A / \partial n_s)_{T, V} = 0$, so that, as $N \ln N$ is constant,

$$w_s = 2kT \frac{\partial}{\partial n_s} \left[- (N - n_s) \ln (N - n_s) - n_s \ln n_s \right]$$

$$= 2kT \left[\ln (N - n_s) + \frac{(N - n_s)}{(N - n_s)} - \ln n_s - \frac{n_s}{n_s} \right]$$

$$= 2kT \ln \frac{(N - n_s)}{n_s}$$

Taking exponentials and rearranging:

$$n_s = (N - n_s) e^{-w_s/2kT} \qquad (8)$$

or, when $n_s \ll N$, i.e. when there are relatively few defects:

$$n_s \simeq N e^{-w_s/2kT} \qquad (9)$$

Another useful form of this relation is obtained by taking decadic logarithms and multiplying both k and w_s by Avogadro's number:

$$\log_{10} \frac{n_s}{N} \simeq \frac{-W_s}{2 \times 2 \cdot 303 \, R \, T} \qquad (10)$$

In this last expression R is the gas constant and W_s is the energy of formation of one mole of Schottky defects. Both equations (9)

† Most books are vague about how large 'sufficiently large' is. It is worth noting that the full Stirling Approximation is excellent even for the smallest factorials: the error is 6 per cent when $x = 2$, 1·5 per cent when $x = 3$, 0·05 per cent when $x = 10$, and negligible above this. On the other hand, the super-Stirling Approximation is still 2 per cent in error when $x = 10^{23}$; the error is 4·5 per cent when $x = 10^{10}$, and 52 per cent when $x = 10$.

and (10) indicate that the relative number of Schottky defects in any MX structure depends only on the absolute temperature and their energy of formation.

It is interesting to apply the formula to a common material like sodium chloride to see how many defects exist at various temperatures. In Chapter 2 it was shown that the lattice energy U_L for sodium chloride is about 180 kcal/mole. This is the energy required to break up one mole of the crystal into gaseous ions at infinite dilution. Schottky-defect formation involves only the removal of ions from the bulk of the crystal to the surface and not to infinity, so W_s must be less than U_L. It turns out to be approximately 45 kcal/mole. Hence

$$\frac{n_s}{N} = 10^{-\frac{45,000}{2 \times 2\cdot303 \times 1\cdot987\,T}} = 10^{-4920/T}$$

Numerical values are tabulated in *Table 4.1*. The results show that,

Table 4.1
Number of Schottky defects at thermodynamic equilibrium in sodium chloride [from equation (10)]

$t°C$	$T°K$	n_s/N	n_s per cm$^{3(a)}$
−273	0	$10^{-\infty}$	0
25	298	3×10^{-17}	5×10^5
200	473	4×10^{-11}	6×10^8
400	673	5×10^{-8}	8×10^{14}
600	873	3×10^{-6}	4×10^{16}
800[b]	1073[b]	3×10^{-5}	4×10^{17}

[a] Calculated using a value of $1\cdot6 \times 10^{22}$ ion pairs per cm^3 for N, as obtained from the density ($1\cdot544$ g/cm^3), the molecular weight ($58\cdot45$ g/mole) and Avogadro's number ($N_0 = 6\cdot023 \times 10^{23}$ ion pairs per mole).

[b] i.e. 1° below the m.p.

near the m.p., one position in 30,000 is vacant; that is, in any one direction in the crystal one lattice position in about 30 is unoccupied. The assumptions made in this treatment will be considered in Section 4.1.3 after the number of Frenkel defects at thermodynamic equilibrium has been calculated.

4.1.2. *Equilibrium Concentration of Frenkel Defects*
The number of Frenkel defects present in a crystal MX at a given temperature is calculated in a similar manner. Let there be N lattice sites per cm^3 in the sublattice affected by Frenkel defects and N^* interstitial positions; let n_f ions leave their lattice sites to go into

interstitial positions, and let w_f be the energy required to create one defect. Then the increase in internal energy ΔU due to the formation of n_f defects is

$$\Delta U = n_f w_f \qquad (11)$$

By the argument given in the preceding section, the number of ways in which n_f ions can be distributed on N^* interstitial sites is

$$p^* = \frac{N^*!}{(N^* - n_f)!\, n_f!} \qquad (12)$$

The n_f vacant sites left can be arranged in p different ways where

$$p = \frac{N!}{(N - n_f)!\, n_f!} \qquad (13)$$

Therefore the increase in entropy during the simultaneous randomization of both the vacant sites and the interstitial ions is

$$\Delta S = k \ln P = k \ln p \,.\, p^*$$

Thus, $\qquad \Delta S = k\left[\ln \frac{N!}{(N - n_f)!\, n_f!} + \ln \frac{N^*!}{(N^* - n_f)!\, n_f!} \right] \qquad (14)$

Combining equations (1), (11) and (14), and minimizing with respect to n_f gives†

$$w_f = kT \ln \frac{(N - n_f)(N^* - n_f)}{n_f^{\,2}} \qquad (15)$$

---

† $\Delta A = \Delta U - T\Delta S$
$\quad = n_f w_f - kT[\ln N! - \ln(N - n_f)! - \ln n_f! + \ln N^*!$
$\qquad\qquad\qquad\qquad\qquad\qquad\qquad\qquad - \ln(N^* - n_f)! - \ln n_f!]$

$(\partial \Delta A / \partial n_f)_{T,\, V} = 0$ at equilibrium, and, as $N!$ and $N^*!$ are independent of n_f

$$w_f = kT \frac{\partial}{\partial n_f}[-\ln(N - n_f)! - \ln(N^* - n_f)! - 2\ln n_f!]$$

Applying the super-Stirling Approximation [equation (6)]

$$w_f \simeq kT \frac{\partial}{\partial n_f}[-(N - n_f)\ln(N - n_f) - (N^* - n_f)\ln(N^* - n_f) - 2n_f \ln n_f]$$

$$= kT\left[\frac{(N - n_f)}{(N - n_f)} + \ln(N - n_f) + \frac{(N^* - n_f)}{(N^* - n_f)} \right.$$
$$\left. + \ln(N^* - n_f) - \frac{2n_f}{n_f} - 2\ln n_f \right]$$

$$= kT \ln \frac{(N - n_f)(N^* - n_f)}{n_f^2}$$

Hence

$$n_f^2 = (N - n_f)(N^* - n_f)\,\mathrm{e}^{-w_f/kT}$$

Neglecting n_f in comparison with N and N^* when the number of defects is small:

$$n_f \simeq \sqrt{(NN^*)}\,\mathrm{e}^{-w_f/2kT} = \sqrt{(NN^*)}\,\mathrm{e}^{-W_f/2RT} \qquad (16)$$

The value of W_f, the energy formation of one mole of Frenkel defects, is usually between 10 and 100 kcal/mole; it will, in general, be different from W_s, the energy of formation of Schottky defects. Hence, there is usually an overwhelming preponderance of either Schottky or Frenkel defects, depending on which process has the smaller energy of formation.

4.1.3. Assumptions and Refinements

The formulae (9) and (16) for the number of Schottky and Frenkel defects at thermodynamic equilibrium have been derived quite generally for all crystals of composition MX, independently of the charges on the ions or the symmetry of the crystal. Formula (16) for Frenkel defects also holds for any binary compound $M_a X_b$ but the treatment for Schottky defects requires slight modification in the general case because the number of vacant cation and anion sites will not be the same, being inversely proportional to the charges on the ions to maintain electroneutrality. For this reason the cation and anion disorder probabilities [equation (4)] will be different.

In addition, four assumptions were implicit in the derivations:

(i) Either Schottky defects or Frenkel defects occurred in a given crystal but not both together. This is normally justifiable because W_s and W_f are generally dissimilar. If they are approximately the same then both types of defect will occur simultaneously; it is a simple matter to extend the theory to this more general case.[1]

(ii) The concentration of defects was sufficiently small that interaction between the defects themselves could be neglected. This is not strictly true and we return to this point later (pp. 78, 174).

(iii) The crystal was held at constant volume so that the energy required to form defects was independent of temperature. Normally crystals are heated at constant pressure which results in an expansion

[1] Wagner, C. and Schottky, W., Z. phys. Chem., **B11** (1930) 163

of the lattice and a temperature-dependent energy of defect formation. This can be allowed for in a more sophisticated treatment.* Thus if the energy of formation of a defect at temperature T is taken to be a linear function of the volume then

$$W_T = W_0 + \alpha V_0 T \left(\frac{\mathrm{d}W}{\mathrm{d}T} \right)$$

where W_0 and W_T are the energies of defect formation at $0°$ and $T°K$, V_0 is the volume at $0°$ and α the thermal expansion coefficient. Substituting this expression in equations (9) and (16) gives

$$n_s = N \, e^{-\left(W_s + \alpha V_0 \frac{T\mathrm{d}W_s}{\mathrm{d}T}\right)/2RT} = BN \, e^{-W_s/2RT} \tag{9a}$$

$$n_f = B\sqrt{(NN^*)} \, e^{-W_f/2RT} \tag{16a}$$

where

$$B = e^{-\frac{\alpha V_0}{2R} \frac{\mathrm{d}W_s}{\mathrm{d}T}} \quad \text{or} \quad e^{-\frac{\alpha V_0}{2R} \frac{\mathrm{d}W_f}{\mathrm{d}T}}$$

As it becomes easier to form defects the larger the volume, $\mathrm{d}W/\mathrm{d}T$ is negative and B is positive. Experiments on cubic crystals at high pressures indicate that B is approximately 50–100 and is expected to be more pronounced for Schottky than for Frenkel defects (see next section). It follows that the values given in *Table 4.1* are too small by one or two orders of magnitude.

(iv) The final assumption in deriving the explicit expressions for the number of defects was that the vibrational frequencies of the ions in the solid were unaffected by the presence of the vacant sites and interstitial ions. This is equivalent to assuming that the entropy of mixing [equations (5) and (14)] is the only entropy effect. This is usually not the case and a pre-exponential correction factor, γ, can be introduced into equations (9a) and (16a) to reflect the small change in vibrational entropy.

$$n_s = \gamma BN \, e^{-W_s/2RT} \tag{9b}$$

$$n_f = \gamma B\sqrt{(NN^*)} \, e^{-W_f/2RT} \tag{16b}$$

For Schottky defects $\gamma = (v/v')^x$ where v is the normal vibration frequency, v' is the frequency of an ion adjacent to a vacant site

* (Note however that Mott and Gurney's treatment[2] of Schottky defects is for a lattice containing only one type of atom and hence their formula differs from equation (9) by a factor 2 in the exponential; it is the appropriate formula for metals and molecular-crystals.)

and x is the coordination number of the vacancy (6 in NaCl-type crystals). As v' is somewhat less than the normal frequency, γ is approximately 10 (i.e. $\sim 1.5^6$). For Frenkel defects the expression for γ is more complicated but it can be seen that, as the frequency of an interstitial ion and that of its neighbours will be greater than that of a normal lattice ion, γ will be less than unity. It will therefore tend to cancel the pre-exponential factor B; thus again the unmodified formula for Frenkel defects is expected to be more reliable as a first estimate than the corresponding formula for Schottky defects.

In this way it can be seen that, although none of the four assumptions is rigorously valid, their adoption simplifies the initial treatment without distorting the general conclusions which can be drawn. These conclusions are that all crystals in thermodynamic equilibrium are subject to lattice defects; and that the concentration of these defects depends exponentially on the temperature and on their energy of formation.

Frenkel defects, by their nature, are likely to be important in crystals with a lattice structure which is sufficiently open to accommodate interstitial ions without much distortion. This is possible for substances of low coordination number, e.g. the zinc blende

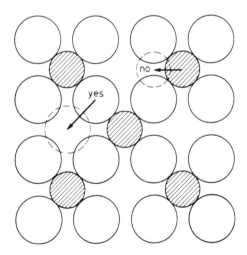

Figure 4.3. Frenkel defects in the anion lattice of an MX_2 compound

The cubic 8:4 coordination is diagrammatically represented by a planar 4:2 lattice; the small shaded circles represent the cations, M, and the larger open circles the anions, X

and zinc oxide structures (see pp. 50, 51). Structures of higher coordination number have little room for interstitial ions and therefore W_f will be very large and hence n_f negligibly small; in such cases (e.g. the alkali halides) Schottky defects are intrinsically probable. When there is considerable disparity of size between M^+ and X^- it will clearly be easier to displace the smaller ion, usually M^+, into the interstitial position. However, even when the cation is smaller than the anion, peculiarities of crystal structure may favour Frenkel defects in the sublattice of the larger anions. Thus in the fluorite-type structure (see p. 54) and in the $PbCl_2$ and PbClF type-structures (see p. 59) only the anion lattice is markedly subject to Frenkel defects because the anions, though physically larger than the cations, have a smaller coordination number (4 instead of 8). This situation is diagrammatically represented in *Figure 4.3*.

4.2. Experimental Investigation of Lattice Defects

Experimental evidence for the existence of Shottky and Frenkel defects has come from a variety of sources and several methods have been used to determine the types of defects present, their energies of formation and heats of interaction. These methods are briefly reviewed in the present section.

4.2.1. *Ionic Conductivity and Self-diffusion*

Electrical conductivity in solids can be electronic or ionic in origin. Electronic conduction occurs typically in metals and in semiconductors (p. 161). Ionic conduction occurs by virtue of the migration of lattice defects under the influence of an applied voltage. An ideal crystal cannot conduct electricity by ionic migration but

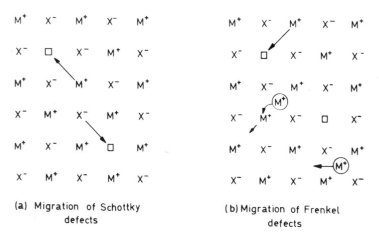

(a) Migration of Schottky defects

(b) Migration of Frenkel defects

Figure 4.4. Migration of defects within a lattice

the presence of defects enables either one or both the ions to transport current by the mechanisms in *Figure 4.4*. The same movements occur randomly in the absence of an electrical field and can be studied as self-diffusion by means of radioactive isotopes. It is clear from *Figure 4.4* that if both cations and anions transport current then Schottky defects must be present since Frenkel defects only enable current to be transported by the ionic sublattice which is subject to the defects. However, unipolar conduction does not necessarily imply a Frenkel mechanism since, even if there are Schottky defects the activation energy for migration of cations and anions need not be the same and one type of current-carrier may predominate. The first extensive studies of ionic transport phenomena in solids were carried out by Tubandt in the 1920s using techniques similar to those used to determine ionic transport numbers in electrolyte solutions. Some numerical data are given in *Table 4.2*.

Table 4.2

Transport numbers t_+ and t_- for some ionic conductors*

Cationic only:	$t_+ = 1{\cdot}00$		Anionic only:	$t_- = 1{\cdot}00$	
Compound	Temperature range		Compound	Temperature range	
LiCl	227–827°		BaF_2	500°	
LiBr	227–827°		$BaCl_2$	400–700°	
LiI	227–827°		$BaBr_2$	350–430°	
AgCl	20–350°		PbF_2	200°	
AgBr	20–350°		$PbCl_2$	200–425°	
AgI	20–400°		$PbBr_2$	250–365°	

Mixed cationic and anionic transport $(t_+ = 1{\cdot}00 - t_-)$

Compound	<400°	400°	500°	550°	600°	650°
NaF	$t_+ = 1{\cdot}00$	1·00	1·00	0·99	0·92	0·86 (at 625°)
NaCl	$t_+ = 1{\cdot}00$	1·00	0·98	0·94	0·91	—
NaBr	$t_+ = 1{\cdot}00$	0·98	0·94	0·92	0·89	—
KCl	$t_+ = 1{\cdot}00$	0·97	0·95	0·92	0·88	0·85
PbI_2	$t_+ : 0{\cdot}00$ (<150°)	0·05 (200°)	0·35 (250°)	0·70 (300°)	0·90 (350°)	0·99 (400°)

* For more complete lists of data see Landolt-Börnstein, Zahlenwerte und Funktionen, 6 Auflage, Teil 6, Elektrische Eigenshaften I, 195.

At temperatures above about 500° most of the alkali halides conduct by both cation and anion migration, indicating the presence of Schottky defects. At lower temperatures the conduction becomes unipolar due to the disparity in activation energies: the halides of

74

sodium, potassium and rubidium become cationic conductors whilst the caesium halides and thallium chloride become predominantly anionic conductors. As expected, the lithium halides remain cationic conductors even up to 800°.

Examples of cationic Frenkel-defect conductors are the silver halides; anionic Frenkel-defect conductors occur with compounds having the fluorite structure and also in lead dichloride and dibromide. Lead diiodide (which has the CdI_2 structure) is subject to Schottky defects and the current is carried by both cations and anions.

In addition to transport-number measurements, the temperature dependence of the electrical conductivity can give information about the migration energies of defects and their heats of formation. The specific electrical conductivity, κ, is given by

$$\kappa = nev \qquad (17)$$

where n is the number of defects, e is their charge and v their mobility. The number of defects is proportional to $e^{-W_s/2RT}$ or $e^{-W_f/2RT}$ and the mobility is proportional to $e^{-U/RT}$ where U is the activation energy for ionic migration. Hence

$$\kappa = \text{const. } e^{-(U + \frac{1}{2}W)RT} \qquad (18)$$

and a plot of $\log \kappa$ against $1/T$ gives the quantity $(U + \frac{1}{2}W)$. The activation energy U can be determined directly by self-diffusion methods using radioisotopes or it can be determined from the temperature variation of conductivity of doped crystals where the number of defects is artificially held constant by the addition of impurity atoms. For example, addition of strontium chloride to potassium chloride creates one vacant cation site for each Sr^{2+} built into the K^+ lattice in order to preserve electrical neutrality. If the constant concentration of defects created in this way is very much greater than the concentration of defects already present due to thermodynamic equilibrium, then any variation in conductivity will be due entirely to the change in mobility; obtaining U in this way enables W to be calculated. The presence of Sr^{2+}, which has a similar radius to K^+ is unlikely to influence the mobility significantly. An even closer matching of radii can be obtained with Na^+ (0·95 Å) and Cd^{2+} (0·97 Å) and here it has been established that the activation energy of migration in the temperature range 250–400° was independent of the mole ratio of Cd^{2+} in the range studied (10^{-5}–10^{-3}). At these temperatures the concentration of Schottky defects in pure sodium chloride (n_s/N) is only about 10^{-8} (see *Table 4.1*).

Some numerical values for the activation energy of ionic migration and for the formation of defects are given in *Table 4.3*; there is some variation in the published values and representative data have been chosen. It can be seen that the energy of defect formation in compounds of stoichiometry MX decreases as the polarization within the lattice increases, being greatest for the alkali metal

Table 4.3

Energies of defect formation, W_s and W_f, and activation energies of ionic migration, U, in kcal/mole

Compound	W_s	U		Compound	W_f	U	
		cation vacancy	anion vacancy			interstitial	vacancy
LiF	61	15·0	—	AgCl	37	3·2	8·5
LiCl	49	9·5	—	AgBr	28	2·6	5·5
LiBr	38	9·0	—	β-AgI	16	3·2	11·3
LiI	31	8·8	—			(α, 1·3)	
NaCl	48	20	26	Ag₂S	—	3·2	—
NaBr	39	20	27	ZnS	90–150*	—	—
KCl	55	18	41	CdTe	24	—	—
KBr	46	7	11	PbS†	40	—	—
CsBr	46	13	6				
CsI	44	13	7	CaF₂	65	38	16
MgO	90–150*	—	62	SrF₂	15	24	—
CaO, SrO, BaO	∼100*	—	—	PbCl₂	—	36	—
CdS	60	—	—	ZrO₂	∼95	25	—
Al₂O₃	470	—	58	UO₂	79	26–30	—

* Calculated value, experimental data not available.
† Type of defect uncertain.

fluorides and chlorides, less for the bromides and iodides and least for the silver halides. For the alkali metal halides W_s is about one-quarter to one-fifth of the total lattice energy U_L and for the alkaline earth oxides it is about one-eighth.

In the compounds considered so far the conductivity is exclusively ionic; frequently there is also an appreciable electronic component and this type of semiconduction will be considered in a later section. Examples of compounds in which the current is carried by both ions and electrons are to be found amongst the sulphides and oxides of the transition elements, e.g. FeS, Ag₂S, FeO, Cu₂O, NiO and ZnO. The cuprous halides also fall in this category between room temperature and 400°; at room temperature and below the cuprous halides are exclusively electronic conductors and above 400° they are essentially pure cation conductors. The temperature at which half the current is carried by each mechanism increases from 225° for CuCl to 275° for CuBr and 325° for CuI.

4.2.2. Density

The presence of small concentrations of Schottky defects lowers the pyknometric density of a crystal whereas small concentrations of Frenkel defects in a stoichiometric crystal leave the density practically unaltered. This is because, as is clear from *Figures 4.1* and *4.2*, creation of Schottky vacancies expands the volume of the crystal whereas the Frenkel vacancies are matched within the crystal volume by an equivalent number of interstitial ions. By contrast, the X-ray density will be virtually independent of the type of defect, or indeed whether point defects are present at all because the X-ray method measures lattice spacings (unit cell dimensions) and these are unaltered by the presence of lattice defects, at least to a first approximation. The effect is difficult to observe since it requires extremely precise X-ray data and extremely sensitive pyknometric measurements.[1] Hitherto the best resolution for changes in density of solids was about 1 part in 10^5 which was frequently insufficient to detect the expected concentration of defects (see *Table 4.1*). However, recent techniques[2] have improved this precision to about 3 parts in 10^7. In this way it was possible to show from the agreement between pyknometric and X-ray densities[3] that silver chloride was subject only to Frenkel defects between room temperature and the melting point, 445°. Similarly, from their lower pyknometric densities, metallic copper, silver, and gold were found to be subject only to Schottky defects. By carefully analysing the data over a range of temperature it was possible to determine not only the proportional number of defects at various temperatures, n_s/N, but also their energy of formation, W_s, e.g.[4]

	Cu	Ag	Au	Pb
$10^4 n_s/N$ (at m.p.)	$2 \cdot 0 \pm 0 \cdot 5$	$1 \cdot 7 \pm 0 \cdot 5$	$7 \cdot 2 \pm 0 \cdot 6$	$2 \cdot 0 \pm 0 \cdot 5$
$W_s (\pm 1$ kcal/mole)	27	25	22	12

When doped or nonstoichiometric crystals are considered, Frenkel type defects may well increase the pyknometric density of the crystal if the supernumerary ions are incorporated in interstitial sites without the corresponding number of vacant sites being

[1] Straumanis, M. E., *Chimia*, **12** (1948) 136
[2] Kuhlmann-Wilsdorf, D. and Sezaki, K., *J. phys. Soc. Japan*, **18** (Suppl. III) (1963) 54
[3] Nicklow, R. M. and Young, R. A., *Phys. Rev.*, **129** (1963) 1936
[4] Simmons, R. P., *Proc. phys. Soc. Japan*, **18** (Suppl. III) (1963) 172, 184

produced. For example, when CaF_2 is doped with YF_3 two possible modes of incorporation could be envisaged:

(a) one cation vacancy for each $3Ca$ replaced by $2Y^{3+}$;
(b) one interstitial F^- for each Y^{3+} added.

Precise pyknometric and X-ray density determinations establish that there is a steady 'anomalous' rise in pyknometric density on progressive addition of yttrium fluoride,[1] thus establishing model (b) as originally predicted by Goldschmidt in 1926.

An interesting repercussion of the inevitable presence of lattice defects in all crystals is in the determination of Avogadro's number, N_0. The most accurate method known is to compare the pyknometric density d with the X-ray unit cell dimensions using the relation

$$N_0 = M/(v_0 d)$$

where v_0 is the volume of the unit cell and M the molecular weight. When a single crystal is formed by slowly pulling a seed crystal from the melt, or when it is heated for annealing, the equilibrium number of inherent thermodynamic defects is formed; when the crystal is cooled to room temperature the number of defects at first decreases but at lower temperatures the activation energy for ionic migration prevents true thermodynamic equilibrium from being established and a large number of defects become frozen in. It is therefore important to choose crystals whose thermal history limits the number of frozen-in defects and whose inherent tendency to defect formation is as small as possible (i.e. W_s and W_f should be large).

4.2.3. Dielectric Polarization and Dielectric Loss

Inspection of *Figure 4.1* indicates that a cation vacancy has an effective negative charge and an anion vacancy has an effective positive charge. These vacancies will therefore tend to attract each other and form a vacancy-pair having a dissociation energy ΔH_{dissoc} which will depend on the dielectric constant, κ, and the distance between the centres of the two vacant sites, r:

$$\Delta H_{\text{dissoc}} \simeq \frac{e^2}{\kappa r}$$

For alkali halides κ is about 5–6 and r is about 2–4 Å hence ΔH_{dissoc} is expected to be approximately 20 kcal/mole, which is about the

---

[1] Short, J. and Roy, R., *J. phys. Chem.*, **67** (1963) 1860

same magnitude as $W_s/2$ [see *Table 4.3*]. Such vacancy-pairs had been invoked to explain the fact that in some crystals a high rate of self-diffusion was accompanied by a low electrical conductivity: the activation energy for diffusion of the vacancy-pair is lower than that of the separate vacancies and therefore permits ready transfer of matter but such pairs cannot contribute to the electrical conductivity which requires independent migration of the vacancies in opposite directions. Direct evidence for vacancy-pairs was first obtained in 1948 from dielectric loss measurements.[1]

In an ideal crystal only electronic and atomic polarization contribute to dielectric phenomena. Electronic polarization involves distortion of the electron cloud of an ion relative to the nucleus and has a resonance frequency in the ultraviolet or visible region; atomic polarization arises from the relative displacement of the positive and negative ions with respect to each other (lattice vibrations) and corresponds to frequencies in the infrared region. In such a crystal, therefore, the dielectric constant should be independent of frequency at audio- or radiofrequencies and there should only be very small dielectric loss. However, if the crystal contains vacancy-pairs which can reorient under the influence of an applied alternating field there will be an anomalous dielectric loss at the appropriate frequency. If τ is the relaxation time for the jump process and τ_0 the time constant of the natural lattice vibrations (as determined from the 'reststrahlen' frequencies) then

$$\tau = \tau_0 \, e^{\Delta E/RT}$$

where ΔE is the height of the potential energy barrier separating equivalent positions of the vacancy-pair.

It is a simple matter to estimate the appropriate frequency for alkali halides; 'reststrahlen' occur at a few hundred cm^{-1} corresponding to $\tau_0 \simeq 2 \times 10^{-13}$ sec, RT is 0·6 kcal/mole, hence $\tau \simeq 10^{-3}$ sec. Relaxation leading to dielectric loss is therefore expected in the kilocycle range of measuring frequencies and the magnitude of the loss will be proportional to the number of ion vacancy-pairs. At higher temperatures the frequencies move into the megacycle range and analysis over a range of temperatures leads to the heat of dissociation of the vacancy pair, ΔH_{dissoc}, and to the fraction of vacancies associated in this way.

Dielectric loss measurement can sometimes also give information about the nature of the defect present. For example, when two loss peaks are observed the results are suggestive of Frenkel defects

---

[1] Breckenridge, R. G., *J. chem. Phys.*, **16** (1948) 959; for a review see R. G. Breckenridge, p. 219 in ref. 1 at end of this chapter.

since, as shown in *Figure 4.5*, there are two types of relaxation with comparable energy:

(a) normal lattice ion moving into vacancy;
(b) interstitial ion moving into vacancy.

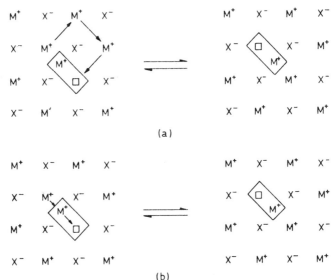

Figure 4.5. Reorientation of a Frenkel defect-pair leading to dielectric loss (a) normal lattice ion moving into vacancy; (b) interstitial ion moving into vacancy

Care must be taken in the interpretation, however, since reorientation of defects arising from adventitious impurity ions may also be observed[1]. Careful studies on potassium chloride, however, have established that, in this case at least, loss is due to self-defects and not impurities[2]; the heat of formation of a vacancy-pair is found to be 30·7 kcal/mole and when this is compared to the heat of formation of a dissociated Schottky defect, 51·2 kcal/mole, the heat of dissociation is found to be ΔH_{dissoc} 20·5 kcal/mole.

Figure 4.6 indicates that there are also two methods for reorientation of a Schottky defect pair: (a) cation motion; (b) anion motion. These mechanisms may occasionally have similar activation energies, particularly when the cation and anion have similar sizes, but

[1] Grimley, T. B., *J. chem. Phys.*, **17** (1949) 496; Freymann, M. and Freymann, R. *J. Phys. Radium, Paris*, **14** (1953) 203; Haven, Y., *J. chem. Phys.*, **21** (1953) 171
[2] Economou, N. A., *Phys. Rev.*, **135** (1964) A1020

more frequently the cation can move much more readily than the larger anion and only one relaxation process is observed.

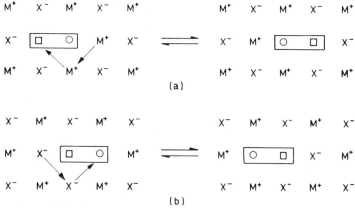

Figure 4.6. Reorientation of a Schottky vacancy-pair leading to dielectric loss (a) cation motion; (b) anion motion

Results obtained in the kilocycle range agree well with those from other methods. For example,[1] the following results were recently obtained for potassium chloride and bromide:

	KCl	KBr
Energy of Schottky defect formation (W_s kcal/mole)	51	55
Energy of dissociation of vacancy-pair (ΔH_{dissoc})	16	16
Activation energy for reorientation of vacancy-pair (ΔE kcal/mole)	21	16

The same type of results can be obtained by studying the mechanical loss in crystals due to stress relaxation when they are subject to elastic vibrations: the maximum damping is observed when the vibration frequency is the same as the jump frequency of the defect-pairs.

4.2.4. Other Methods

Information about inherent lattice defects has also been obtained from specific heat data, from nuclear magnetic resonance, electron spin resonance, Mössbauer spectroscopy, and theoretical calculations. These methods will now briefly be considered.

The formation of lattice defects requires energy. Mott and Gurney therefore predicted that there would be an anomalous rise in the

[1] Sack, H. S. and Smith, G. C. S., *J. phys. Soc., Japan*, **18** (Suppl. III) (1963) 1240

G

molar heat capacity of crystals at higher temperatures as the defect concentration became appreciable. The effect was first observed for silver bromide[1] where the high concentration of defects in the last 250° before the melting point was particularly favourable. Appropriate analysis leads to the number of defects and their heat of formation. Thus for silver bromide $W_f = 29\cdot2$ kcal/mole and $n_f/N \simeq 3\cdot7$ per cent just below the m.p. at 420°.

Nuclear magnetic resonance in solids can be used to detect interactions between lattice defects and either the nuclear magnetic dipole or the nuclear electric quadrupole moment. When magnetic dipoles are being considered, lattice vacancies and interstitial ions will have a pronounced effect on the spin-lattice relaxation time and hence on the resonance line-width. At higher temperatures diffusion of the defects also affects the nuclear spin resonance. Similarly, the crystalline electric field will be disturbed by the presence of defects and the resulting electric field gradient will interact with the electrical quadrupole moment of nuclei having a spin quantum number $I > \frac{1}{2}$. This latter effect is large for dislocations but is less important for vacancies or interstitial ions unless their concentration is higher than 0·1 per cent. The magnetic and electric quadrupole interactions with defects are therefore complementary. When impurity ions are present there is an additional effect due to the differences in ionic charge.

Electron spin resonance is of limited use for investigating inherent defects in stoichiometric crystals since it relies on the presence of unpaired electrons on the species being studied. However, it is mentioned here for completeness since it can occasionally be used on such systems. The technique finds extensive application in investigating F-centres (i.e. electrons trapped in vacant lattice sites), excitons, impurity centres in semiconductors and free valencies at grain boundaries. Some of these phenomena will be discussed in later chapters.

Mössbauer spectroscopy makes use of the nuclear resonance fluorescence which occurs during the recoil-less emission and resonant reabsorption of γ-rays.[2] Lattice defects may change several of the properties of individual ions or the collective properties of the crystal and these in turn alter the Mössbauer spectrum. For example, change in electron distribution around a defect ion

[1] Kanzaki, H., *Phys. Rev.*, **81** (1951) 884; Christie, R. W. and Lawson, A. W., *J. chem. Phys.*, **19** (1951) 517

[2] Wertheim, G. K., *Mössbauer Effect: Principles and Applications*, Academic Press, New York, 1964; Greenwood, N. N., '*The Mössbauer Spectra of Chemical Compounds*', *Chem. in Br.*, (1967) 56.

(whether an inherent interstitial or an impurity ion) will alter its chemical shift, δ, i.e. the position of the line in the spectrum. Localized lattice modes in the vicinity of the defect might alter the recoil-free fraction, f, which depends sensitively on the lattice vibration frequencies and force constants; this would be reflected in a change in intensity of the absorption line. Asymmetries near the defect lead to the creation of electric field gradients, or to a change in their magnitude; this results in a quadrupole splitting of the line, Δ, and may also make the intensity of the effect directionally dependent. If the defect leads to a range of symmetries around the ion being studied, these several field gradients may lead to a broadening or distortion of the line shape rather than to a resolved quadrupole multiplet. In short, if they are present in sufficient concentration, lattice defects can alter the position, intensity, multiplicity or shape of the Mössbauer resonance lines. The concentration of defects required depends on the particular element being studied and the conditions of the experiment, but in the favourable case of enriched iron or tin, the concentrations can be as low as 10^{-4}–10^{-3}. The technique has also proved particularly valuable in studying nonstoichiometric compounds (see also p. 101).

The final technique for studying lattice defects is theoretical rather than experimental. The energy of formation of Schottky and Frenkel defects can be calculated using models similar to those discussed in Chapter 2 for lattice energies. Here, however, the estimation of polarization energies becomes crucial to the success of the model. This can be illustrated by considering in detail the process of forming one Schottky defect. The process can be divided into three steps:

(a) removal of one M^+ and one X^- from separated lattice sites within the crystal to infinity;
(b) bringing M^+ and X^- from infinity to lattice sites on the surface of the crystal;
(c) relaxation of ions around the vacancies so formed.

Process (a) requires an energy w_1 equal to the lattice energy for one pair of ions (see p. 18):

$$w_1 = \frac{Ae^2}{r_0}\left(1 - \frac{\rho}{r_0}\right)$$

Process (b) evolves energy equivalent to $w_1/2$ since the Madelung constant for surface ions involves summation over a hemisphere only, the other hemisphere being outside the crystal and unoccupied by ions. In the absence of relaxation effects, therefore, the energy

83

LATTICE DEFECTS

of Schottky defect formation would be just half the lattice energy: $w_s = w_1/2$ or, multiplying by Avogadro's number, $W_s = \frac{1}{2}U_L$. However, the ions around a cation vacancy will be polarized as if the vacancy carried a virtual negative charge. Similarly an anion vacancy carries a virtual positive charge. This results in relaxation processes in which the ions move in the directions indicated in *Figure 4.7* (the displacement is shown for the first two coordination shells only for simplicity).

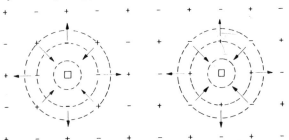

Figure 4.7. Relaxation of ions around a cation vacancy and an anion vacancy

On the basis of classical dielectric theory the cation vacancy can be treated as a spherical cavity of charge $-e$ inside a homogeneous material of dielectric constant κ. If, as a first approximation, the radius of the cavity is taken to be the radius of the cation, r_+, then the polarization energy will be

$$P_+ = \frac{-e^2}{2r_+}\left(1 - \frac{1}{\kappa}\right)$$

Similarly

$$P_- = \frac{-e^2}{2r_-}\left(1 - \frac{1}{\kappa}\right)$$

Remembering that the internuclear distance $r_0 = (r_+ + r_-)$ the energy of Schottky defect formation becomes

$$w_s = \frac{Ae^2}{2(r_+ + r_-)}\left[1 - \frac{\rho}{(r_+ + r_-)}\right] - \frac{e^2}{2}\left(1 - \frac{1}{\kappa}\right)\left(\frac{1}{r_+} + \frac{1}{r_-}\right)$$

Hence

$$W_s = \frac{1}{2}U_L - \frac{1}{2}N_0 e^2\left(1 - \frac{1}{\kappa}\right)\left(\frac{1}{r_+} + \frac{1}{r_-}\right)$$

84

The energy of Schottky defect formation is therefore rather less than half the lattice energy and detailed evaluation depends on estimates of two factors:

(a) the value selected for the dielectric constant in the region of the defect; this is frequently taken to be the bulk dielectric constant of the crystal; and

(b) the values used for the radii of the cavities formed by relaxation around the cation vacancy and anion vacancy.

Early calculations[1] gave the following values which can be compared with the more-recent experimental data in *Table 4.3*: $W_s(NaCl)$ 43 kcal/mole, $W_s(KCl)$ 48 kcal/mole, $W_s(KBr)$ 42 kcal/mole. The calculations have since been refined and extended to include energies of interaction between defect-pairs[2] and the most recent work,[3] which includes terms for coulomb, repulsion, and polarization energies and also for the energy of lattice strain in the neighbourhood of the distortion caused by the defect, gives results in complete agreement with experiment: $W_s(NaCl)$ 48·3 kcal/mole, $W_s(KCl)$ 59·3 kcal/mole. It is, of course, also possible to calculate the energy of formation of hypothetical defects; for example, the energy of formation of Frenkel defects in sodium chloride is $W_f(NaCl)$ 67 kcal/mole, thus confirming the virtual absence of interstitial ions in the close-packed six-coordinate structure.

The techniques for investigating lattice defects discussed in this section have been confined almost entirely to those methods used for studying inherent defects in stoichiometric crystals. A further range of techniques becomes available when deviations from stoichiometry occur but discussion of these is deferred until Chapters 6 and 7.

References for Further Reading

1. Shockley, W., Hollomon, J. H., Maurer, R. and Seitz, F., *Imperfections in Nearly Perfect Crystals*, Wiley, New York, 1952
2. Mott, N. F. and Gurney, R. W., *Electronic Processes in Ionic Crystals* (2nd edn), Oxford University Press, 1964
3. Jacobs, P. W. M. and Tompkins, F. C., *Q. Rev.*, 6 (1952) 238–261
4. Stone, F. S., 'Lattice Defects in Ionic Crystals', Chapter 2 in Garner, W. E. (Ed.), *Chemistry of the Solid State*, Butterworths, London, 1955

[1] Mott, N. F. and Littleton, M. J., *Trans. Faraday Soc.*, 34 (1938) 485
[2] Dienes, G. J., *J. chem. Phys.*, 16 (1948) 620
[3] Scholtz, A., *Phys. Status Solidi*, 7 (1964) 973

5. Rees, A. L. G., *Chemistry of the Defect Solid State*, Methuen, London, 1954
6. Van Gool, W., *Principles of Defect Chemistry of Crystalline Solids*, Academic Press, New York, 1966

5

SPECIFIC DEFECT STRUCTURES IN STOICHIOMETRIC CRYSTALS

AT the beginning of the preceding chapter, equilibrium atomic defects were classified under two main headings: those which were inherently present in all crystals because of the thermodynamic conditions of equilibrium, and those which were specific or characteristic of the particular crystalline compound considered. Specific defects can themselves be classified under two subsections: specific defects in stoichiometric crystals (discussed in this Chapter) and defects arising from nonstoichiometry (discussed in Chapter 6).

There are many ways in which specific defects can be introduced in stoichiometric crystals and a general classification is less profitable than an enumeration of particular examples to indicate the range of behaviour encountered. However, the cohering theme is the ability of a crystal structure or of one of its sublattices to become disordered.

5.1. Order–disorder Phenomena

The simplest type of specific defect is when an ordered lattice (sometimes called a superlattice) becomes disordered by place-exchange as in *Figure 5.1*. The phenomenon was predicted by Tammann in 1919 and first observed for the intermetallic compound

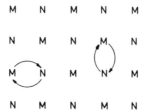

Figure 5.1. The disordering of a superlattice by place-exchange

Cu_3Au in 1923 and for CuAu in 1925. Its occurrence will clearly be restricted to compounds (alloys) where M and N are similar and it is most unlikely to occur in ionic compounds such as M^+X^- because of the large electrostatic repulsions that would ensue.

In fact, it has only been observed in alloys of the type MN (e.g. CuAu, β-brass-CuZn, CuPd, CuPt, NiAl, FeAl etc.) and M_3N (e.g. Cu_3Au, Cu_3Pd, Cu_3Pt, Ni_3Fe, Ni_3Mn, Fe_3Si, Fe_3Al, etc.), and in a few ternary systems such as the Heusler alloys. A detailed treatment is therefore inappropriate in a book on ionic crystals, but it is important to visualize the phenomenon and some of its consequences as it is relevant to the disordering of sublattices in ionic compounds. Structural features are considered first and then the effect of these on physical properties.

When both components of the alloy form face-centred-cubic lattices (and in certain other cases also), the superlattice of the alloy will be cubic-close-packed and its detailed structure will depend on the relative concentrations of the two constituents. The M_3N superlattice (e.g. Cu_3Au) is shown in *Figure 5.2(a)*; when this is heated the two sets of sites become progressively more randomly occupied until, above a certain critical temperature, disorder is complete as indicated in *Figure 5.2(b)* and for every lattice site in the

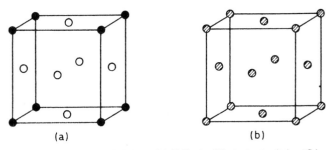

(a) superlattice of Cu_3Au (● Au, ○ Cu); (b) disordered Cu_3Au structure (⊘ Au or Cu)

Figure 5.2. Order–disorder in cubic-close-packed alloys M_3N

crystal there is a probability of $1:4$ of finding an Au atom and a probability of $3:4$ of finding a Cu atom. The phase remains cubic-close-packed throughout but, because of the regular way the atoms are packed in the superlattice it is primitive cubic rather than face-centred cubic (compare *Figure 5.2(a)* carefully with *Figure 3.5*, NaCl). The stoichiometry Cu_3Au arises in *Figure 5.2(a)* because the six open circles (Cu) are shared between two adjacent unit cells and therefore represent three copper atoms whereas the eight solid circles (Au) are each shared between eight contiguous unit cells and, therefore, jointly represent only one gold atom. If the Cu atoms in the top and bottom faces of the cell are replaced by Au atoms, then the stoichiometry becomes CuAu and a layer-lattice results as shown in *Figure 5.3(a)*. This incorporates eight unit cells for clarity and represents the ordered or superlattice structure of CuAu. Because of the layering the lattice no longer has cubic symmetry but is tetragonal with an axial ratio $c/a = 0.932$. When this ordered array is heated, randomization gradually sets in until, in the completely disordered state, the cubic structure shown in *Figure 5.3(b)* is obtained. This is identical with *Figure 5.2(b)* except that there is now an equal probability of finding a copper or a gold atom on any site.

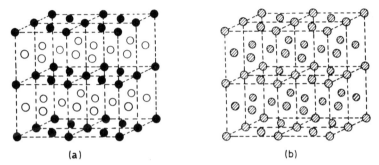

(a)   (b)

(a) superlattice of CuAu (● Au, ○ Cu); (b) disordered CuAu structure (⊘ Au or Cu)

Figure 5.3. Order–disorder in cubic close-packed alloys MN

For body-centred-cubic alloys two kinds of superlattice are also possible. If the constituents are present in equal amounts as in FeAl or β-brass (CuZn), then the caesium chloride structure is adopted in ordered specimens at room temperature [*Figure 5.4(a)*] but this becomes progressively randomized at higher temperatures until the structure is completely disordered as in *Figure 5.4(b)*. Rather more complex behaviour is encountered when the stoichiometry approaches M_3N. If, in *Figure 5.4(a)* one-half of the Al atoms (●) are replaced in a regular manner by Fe atoms(○), then the structure shown in *Figure 5.5(a)* is obtained. This represents one unit cell of the ordered superlattice of Fe_3Al. On becoming disordered, however, only the aluminium atoms and one-third of the iron atoms become randomized as shown by ⊘ in *Figure 5.5(b)*; the other two-thirds of the iron atoms remain ordered. The unit cell is now only one-eighth of the volume shown in *Figure 5.5(b)*. This is an important example because only one of the sublattices becomes disordered; it therefore leads naturally to the phenomena of specific defects in ionic crystals to be discussed in subsequent sections.

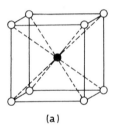
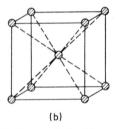

(a)   (b)

(a) superlattice of FeAl (● Al, ○ Fe); (b) disordered FeAl structure (● Al or Fe)

Figure 5.4. Order–disorder in FeAl

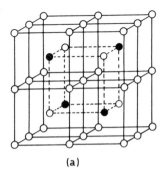
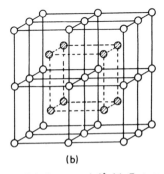

(a)   (b)

(a) Superlattice of Fe₃Al; the body centres of the simple cubic lattice composed of $\frac{2}{3}$ of the Fe atoms (○), are occupied regularly by Al (●) and the rest of the Fe atoms (○); (b) The disordered Fe₃Al structure
(○ Fe, ⊘ Fe or Al)

Figure 5.5. Order–disorder in Fe₃Al

The formation of a superlattice on cooling a disordered alloy is accompanied by changes in several of the physical properties of the alloy. Thus there is an increase in density because of the more favourable packing conditions and an increase in ductility because of the greater regularity within the crystal planes. For the same reason, there is a large increase in the electrical conductivity because there is less resistive scattering of the conduction electrons by the ordered array of atoms. We have also seen that the ordering may lead to a decrease in crystallographic symmetry whereas the dis-ordered phase is always cubic. Finally, the ordering process is accompanied by the gradual evolution of heat and this manifests itself as a specific heat anomaly. All these effects can be used to follow the order–disorder transformation; specific heat and X-ray methods have been most used but changes in conductivity and magnetic properties have also been extensively studied.

The order–disorder transformation is a cooperative phenomenon like the onset of 'rotation' in crystals and the loss of ferromagnetism at the Curie point. It frequently occurs over a temperature range of several hundred degrees as can be seen from the specific heat plots in *Figure 5.6*. In each case the dotted curve indicates the expected increase in specific heat in the absence of any disordering phenomenon; thus, when β-brass for example is heated above 120° energy is required not only for the increased vibrational motion of the atoms, but also to enable some of the atoms to exchange places. Once the disordering has started, the process rapidly increases [*Figure 5.6(a)*] until at about 470° the phase is

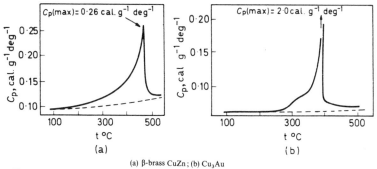

(a) β-brass CuZn; (b) Cu₃Au

Figure 5.6. Specific heat anomalies accompanying order–disorder transformations

almost completely disordered. The specific heat then returns to a value only slightly above the value it would have had if the disordering process had not occurred. The case of Cu₃Au [*Figure 5.6(b)*] is somewhat different; not only is there a specific heat anomaly due to the disordering, but there is also a latent heat effect which is required to dissipate the short range order within the minute 'nuclei' which remain of the phase of lower symmetry.

The possibility of rearranging a random array of atoms to form a superlattice depends on the thermal energy of the atoms (temperature) the difference in energies of the disordered and ordered states, and the height of the energy barrier for atom-place-exchange. If the difference in energies between the disordered and ordered states is too large (as it is in ionic crystals) then disordering by place exchange does not occur. Conversely if the difference in energies is very small, then ordering never occurs; this is the situation with silver–gold alloys since the two components have similar electronic structures and electronegativities and very similar atomic sizes because of the lanthanide contraction (Ag 1·444 Å, Au 1·442 Å). It is only when copper ($1\cdot278$ Å) is combined with gold that sufficient difference exists to achieve a gain in energy on ordering.

A more detailed treatment of order–disorder transformations will be found in several of the references at the end of this chapter. It should also be mentioned that the phenomenon is also observed over a range of compositions and is not restricted merely to the ideal stoichiometric formulae MN and M_3N.

5.2. Normal and Inverse Spinel Structures

Spinels form a large class of inorganic crystals whose structure is related to that of the mineral spinel itself, $MgAl_2O_4$. The general formula is AB_2X_4. It will be convenient to describe the spinel-type structure and to list the ions which adopt it before discussing defect spinel structures. The unit cell contains thirty-two oxide ions in almost perfect cubic-close-packed array, and corresponds to the formula $A_8B_{16}O_{32}$. In the normal spinel structure the eight A ions occupy tetrahedral sites in the face-centred-cubic oxide lattice and the sixteen B ions occupy octahedral sites as indicated in *Figure 5.7*. The structure is closely related to those of sodium chloride and cubic zinc sulphide (*Figure 3.5*); if all the cubelets in *Figure 5.7*

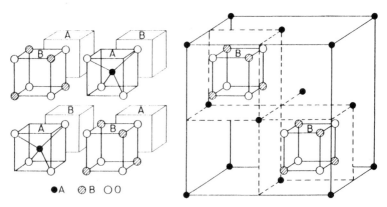

Figure 5.7. Spinel structure AB_2O_4. The structure can be thought of as eight octants of alternating AO_4 tetrahedra and B_4O_4 cubes as shown in the left-hand diagram; the 4O have the same orientation in all eight octants and so build up into a face-centred cubic lattice of 32 ions which coordinate A tetrahedrally and B octahedrally. The four A octants contain 4 A ions and the four B octants contain 16 B ions. The unit cell is completed by an encompassing face-centred cube of A ions (●) as shown in the right-hand diagram; this is shared with adjacent unit cells and comprises the remaining 4 A ions in the complete unit cell $A_8B_{16}O_{32}$. The location of two of the B_4O_4 cubes is shown for orientation.

were B-type the structure would be that of sodium chloride, if all were A-type it would be cubic zinc sulphide; spinel can therefore be considered as a regular alternation of fragments of these two structures. The structure, though regular, is somewhat complex and can best be appreciated from studying a model. This can readily be constructed from the information given in *Figure 5.8* which

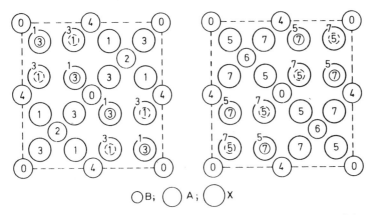

Figure 5.8. Plan of the spinel unit cell, AB_2X_4, projected on to the base of the cell. The heights of the atoms are indicated in units of $\frac{1}{8} a_0$. For clarity the lower and upper halves of the cell are shown separately

shows the projection on a cube face of the atoms in the lower half of the unit cell and indicates the heights of the various atoms above the face in terms of fractions of the unit-cell dimension a_0. For an ideal face-centred-cubic oxide lattice the positions are as shown, defined by a parameter $u = 0.375$ (i.e. $\frac{3}{8}$); frequently, however, there are small distortions and u varies from 0.375 to 0.392. Thus for spinel itself ($MgAl_2O_4$) $u = 0.387$. Because of the regularity of this distortion within the eight segments (2^3) of the unit cell the overall symmetry of the total unit cell is accurately cubic.

The two factors which determine the combinations of atoms which can form a spinel-type structure are the total cation charge and the relative cation sizes. For oxides of the formula AB_2O_4 there are eight negative charges to be balanced and this can be achieved by the following three combinations of cation charges: ($A^{2+} + 2B^{3+}$), ($A^{4+} + 2B^{2+}$) and ($A^{6+} + 2B^+$). These are sometimes referred to as 2,3, 4,2 and 6,1 spinels respectively. The 2,3 spinels are by far the most numerous and account for 80 per cent of the known cases:

The anion can be O^{2-}, S^{2-}, Se^{2-} or Te^{2-};

A^{2+} can be Mg, Ca; Cr, Mn, Fe, Co, Ni, Cu; Zn, Cd, Hg; or Sn

B^{3+} can be Al, Ga, In; Ti, V, Cr, Mn, Fe, Co, Ni; or Rh

Reference to *Table 3.1* shows that most of the bivalent cations have radii in the range 0·65–1·0 Å and indeed the large ions Ca^{2+} (0·99 Å) and Hg (1·10 Å) do not occur in oxide spinels. The radii of the tervalent cations fall predominantly in the range 0·6–0·76 Å, only Al^{3+} (0·50 Å) and In^{3+} (0·81 Å) falling outside this range.

The 4,2 spinels are the next most numerous category and account for about 15 per cent of the known spinels:

The anion can be O^{2-} or S^{2-};

A^{4+} can be Ti, V, Mo, (Si), Ge, Sn, or Pb;

B^{2+} can be Mg, Mn, Fe, Co, Ni, Cu, or Zn

Examples are $TiMg_2O_4$, $PbFe_2O_4$, and $SnCu_2S_4$.

The least favoured charge combination is 6,1. Only oxide systems are known, presumably because of the highly polarizing nature of the +6 cations and even with the oxides there is probably considerable tendency towards covalency. Spinels of this type include $MoAg_2O_4$, $MoNa_2O_4$, WNa_2O_4 and the high temperature forms of $MoLi_2O_4$ and WLi_2O_4.

It is not necessary for the anion to be bivalent. For example, spinels with univalent anions are known: these require a total cation charge of +4, thereby limiting the combination of cation charges to $A^{2+}B_2^+X_4$. Typical examples are $NiLi_2F_4$, $ZnK_2(CN)_4$, $CdK_2(CN)_4$, and $ZnK_2(CN)_4$; it is important to note that these compounds are cubic, three-dimensional lattices and not discrete coordination complexes such as $K_2[Zn(CN)_4]$, etc. The compound Cu_3Cl_4 also has this structure, one of the copper ions being in the +2 state and the other two in the +1 oxidation state.

Many of the spinel-type compounds formed by combinations of the ions mentioned above do not have the normal structure in which the A cations are in tetrahedral sites and the B cations are in octahedral sites; instead they adopt the inverse spinel structure in which half the B cations occupy the tetrahedral sites whilst the other half of the B cations and all the A cations are distributed on the octahedral sites. This is therefore a specific defect structure since all crystallographically identical sites within the unit cell are not occupied by the same cation. In contrast to disordered alloys, however, the randomization does not affect the whole structure but only one of the three sublattices. Normal and inverse spinels are limiting cases and various degrees of 'inversion' are sometimes observed or even complete randomization of both A and B cations on all tetrahedral (t) and octahedral (o) sites in the unit cell. The degree of disorder is conveniently represented by a parameter λ, the fraction of B cations in tetrahedral sites. For a normal spinel $\lambda = 0$, i.e. $(A)_t[B_2]_oO_4$; for an inverse spinel $\lambda = \frac{1}{2}$, i.e. $(B)_t[AB]_oO_4$; intermediate values are also possible and for $\lambda = \frac{1}{3}$ there is complete randomization of both A and B, e.g. $NiAl_2O_4$. The degree of inversion of most of the known spinels has been established and the results are summarized in *Table 5.1* which lists the charge-type, the value of the parameter λ, the unit-cell dimension, a_o, and the distortion parameter u. The parameter λ is not necessarily constant but may vary with temperature. For example, the compound $MgFe_2O_4$ in *Table 5.1* is normally regarded as being inverse, $(Fe)_t[MgFe]_oO_4$ though in fact there is a somewhat random, temperature-dependent distribution given by $(Fe_{2\lambda}Mg_{1-2\lambda})_t[Mg_{2\lambda}Fe_{2(1-\lambda)}]_oO_4$ where λ increases with temperature according to the expression:

$$\frac{(1 - \lambda)(1 - 2\lambda)}{2\lambda^2} = e^{-E/RT}$$

Here E is the increase in energy resulting from the interchange of Mg^{2+} on octahedral sites with Fe^{3+} on tetrahedral sites and equals 2·42 kcal/mole.

To understand why some spinels tend to give the inverse structure it is necessary to consider four factors:

(*a*) the relative sizes of A and B;
(*b*) the Madelung constants for the normal and inverse structures;
(*c*) the influence of ligand field stabilization energies; and
(*d*) polarization or covalency effects.

Simple radius ratio theory (Chapter 3 Section 3.2) predicts that cations with ρ in the range 0·414–0·732 prefer octahedral coordination, whilst smaller cations with ρ between 0·225 and 0·414 would preferentially occupy the tetrahedral sites. As trivalent cations, B^{3+}, are frequently smaller than bivalent cations, A^{2+}, there is a tendency for them to occupy the tetrahedral sites; however, there are only enough tetrahedral sites to accommodate half the B^{3+} cations, so the other half randomize with the A^{2+} cations on the octahedral sites. If this were the only factor operating, then all spinels for which the radius of B^{3+} was smaller than the radius of A^{2+} would adopt the inverse configuration. This is far from being the case because coulombic interactions tend to act in the opposite direction as discussed in the next paragraph.

95

Table 5.1

Detailed structure of some spinels

Type	Compound	a_0 Å	u	Type	Compound	a_0 Å	u
	Normal $(\lambda = 0\cdot00)$				*Normal* $(\lambda = 0\cdot00)$		
2,3	$MgAl_2O_4$	8·086	0·387	2,1	$ZnK_2(CN)_4$	12·54	0·37
	$MgTi_2O_4$	8·474			$CdK_2(CN)_4$	12·84	0·37
	MgV_2O_4	8·413	0·385		$HgK_2(CN)_4$	12·76	0·37
	$MgCr_2O_4$	8·333	0·385	6,1	$MoNa_2O_4$	8·99	
	$MgMn_2O_4$	8·07 (c 9·28)	0·385		WNa_2O_4	8·99	
	$MgRh_2O_4$	8·530			$MoAg_2O_4$	9·26	0·364
	$MnTi_2O_4$	8·600		4,2	$GeMg_2O_4$ high press	8·255	
	MnV_2O_4	8·522	0·388		$GeFe_2O_4$	8·411	0·375
	$MnCr_2O_4$	8·437			$GeCo_2O_4$	8·317	0·375
	Mn_3O_4	8·13			$GeNi_2O_4$	8.221	0·375
	$MnRh_2O_4$	8·613			*Inverse* $(\lambda = 0\cdot50)$		
	$FeCr_2O_4$	8·377					
	$CoAl_2O_4$	8·105	0·390	2,3	$MgIn_2O_4$	8·81	0·372
	CoV_2O_4	8·407			Fe_3O_4	8·394	0·379
	$CoCr_2O_4$	8·332			*$FeCo_2O_4$	8·254	
	$CoMn_2O_4$	8·1 (c 9·3)			$FeGa_2O_4$	8·360	
	Co_3O_4	8·083			$CoFe_2O_4$	8·390	
	$CoRh_2O_4$	8·495			*$NiMn_2O_4$	8·39	0·383
	$NiCr_2O_4$	8·248 (c 8·454)			$NiFe_2O_4$	8·325	0·381
	$NiRh_2O_4$	8·36 (c 8·67)			*$NiCo_2O_4$	8·121	
	$CuCr_2O_4$	8·532 (c 7·788)			$NiGa_2O_4$	8·258	0·387
	$CuMn_2O_4$	8·33	0·390		$CuFe_2O_4$	8·445	0·380
	$CuRh_2O_4$	8·702 (c 7·914)			$MgIn_2S_4$	10·687	<0·387
	$ZnAl_2O_4$	8·086			$CrAl_2S_4$	9·914	0·384
	ZnV_2O_4	8·414			$CrIn_2S_4$	10·59	0·386
	$ZnCr_2O_4$	8·327			$FeIn_2S_4$	10·598	<0·387
	$ZnMn_2O_4$	8·087 (c 9·254)			$CoIn_2S_4$	10·559	0·384
	$ZnFe_2O_4$	8·416	0·380		$NiIn_2S_4$	10·464	0·384
	$ZnCo_2O_4$	8·047		2,1	$NiLi_2F_4$	8·31	0·381
	$ZnGa_2O_4$	8·37		4,2	$TiMg_2O_4$	8·445	0·390
	$ZnRh_2O_4$	8·54			VMg_2O_4	8·39	0·386
	$CdCr_2O_4$	8·567	0·385		$SnMg_2O_4$	8·60	
	$CdMn_2O_4$	8·22 (c 9·87)			$TiMn_2O_4$	8·67	
	$CdFe_2O_4$	8·69			$SnMn_2O_4$	8·865	
	$CdGe_2O_4$	8·39			$TiFe_2O_4$	8·50	0·390
	$CdRh_2O_4$	8·781			$TiCo_2O_4$	8·465	
	$CaIn_2S_4$	10·774	<0·393		VCo_2O_4	8·379	
	$MnCr_2S_4$	10·129			$SnCo_2O_4$	8·644	0·375
	$FeCr_2S_4$	9·998			$TiZn_2O_4$	8·445	0·380
	$CoCr_2S_4$	9·934			VZn_2O_4	8·38	
	$CoRh_2S_4$	9·71			$SnZn_2O_4$	8·665	0·390
	$CuTi_2S_4$	9·880	0·382		*Partly Inverse* $(0\cdot00 < \lambda < 0\cdot50)$		
	CuV_2S_4	9·824	0·384				
	$CuCr_2S_4$	9·629	0·381	2,3	$MgFe_2O_4$ $(\lambda\,0\cdot45)$	8·389	0·382
	$CuRh_2S_4$	9·72			$MgGa_2O_4$ $(\lambda\,0\cdot33)$	8·280	0·379
	$ZnAl_2S_4$	9·988	0·384		$MnAl_2O_4$ $(\lambda\,0\cdot15)$	8·242	
	$ZnCr_2S_4$	9·983			$MnFe_2O_4$ $(\lambda\,0\cdot10)$	8·507	0·835
	$CdCr_2S_4$	10·207	0·375		$MnGa_2O_4$ $(\lambda\,0\cdot10)$	8·435	
	$CdIn_2S_4$	10·797	0·386		$FeMn_2O_4$ $(\lambda\,0\cdot33)$	8·31 (c 8·85)	
	$HgCr_2S_4$	10·206	0·392		$CoGa_2O_4$ $(\lambda\,0\cdot45)$	8·307	
	$HgIn_2S_4$	10·812	<0·403		$NiAl_2O_4$ $(\lambda\,0\cdot375)$	8·046	0·831
	$CuCr_2Se_4$	10·365	0·380		$CuAl_2O_4$ $(\lambda\,0\cdot20)$	8·086	
	$ZnCr_2Se_4$	10·443	~0·378		$MnIn_2S_4$ $(\lambda\,0\cdot33)$	10·694	<0·390
	$CdCr_2Se_4$	10·721	0·383	4,2	VMn_2O_4 $(\lambda\,0\cdot40)$	8·575	0·382
	$CuCr_2Te_4$	11·049	0·379				

* $\sim(Co^{2+})_i[Fr^{3+}Co^{3+}]_oO_4$; $\sim(Co^{2+})_i[Co^{3+}Ni^{3+}]_oO_4$; $(Mn^{2+}_{\frac{1}{2}}Mn^{3+}_{\frac{1}{2}})_i[Ni^{2+}(Mn^{3+}_{\frac{1}{2}}Mn^{4+}_{\frac{1}{2}})]_oO_4$

The Madelung constant for an array of ions in the normal spinel configuration will, in general, be different from the Madelung constant for the inverse arrangement. Other things being equal, the configuration with the higher Madelung constant will be the more stable since this corresponds to a greater lattice energy. The problem is one of some subtlety because distortions in the oxide-ion positions must normally occur to accommodate the two sets of cations of different radius and this also affects the lattice energy. Detailed calculations of the Madelung constant of 2,3 spinels in terms of the distortion parameter u have been carried out[1] and the results (*Table 5.2*) show that for all values of $u > 0.379$ the normal configuration has the larger Madelung constant and thus is more

Table 5.2
Madelung constants of normal and inverse
2,3 spinels as a function of the parameter u

u	A (normal)	A (inverse)
0·375	128·6	130·7
0·380	131·4	131·0
0·385	134·0	131·2
0·390	136·5	131·4

stable than the inverse configuration. Accordingly, very few 2,3 spinels with spherically symmetrical cations adopt the inverse configuration. By contrast, electrostatic interactions ensure that 4,2 spinels are almost invariably inverse because the cation with the higher charge goes to the site of higher coordination,

$$(B^{2+})_t[A^{4+}B^{2+}]_oO_4.$$

The only exceptions are spinels containing germanium; these are normal, with germanium in the tetrahedral sites. It is noteworthy in this connexion that the quadrivalent cations which are known to occur in the spinel-type structures are among the larger M^{4+} species and all except germanium ($\rho = 0.38$) have a radius ratio $\rho > 0.414$ appropriate for sixfold coordination. If, in the inverse 4,2 spinel, there is a complete randomization of A^{4+} and B^{2+} on the octahedral sites then the Madelung constant is the same as for the normal 2,3 spinel. *Figure 5.9* shows that this lies above the Madelung constant for normal 4,2 spinels only if $u > 0.385$. However, a further gain in electrostatic energy ensues if the octahedral

[1] Verwey, E. J. W., de Boer, F., and Van Santen, J. H., *J. chem. Phys.*, **16** (1948) 1091; de Boer, F., Van Santen, J. H., and Verwey, E. J. W., *J. chem. Phys.*, **17** (1950) 1032

H

sites in the inverse 4,2 spinel are ordered instead of random. This gain is shown by the dotted line in *Figure 5.9* which indicates that inversion of all 4,2 spinels with $u > 0.380$ is expected. This is found experimentally except for the germanium spinels mentioned above and considered further at the end of the next paragraph.

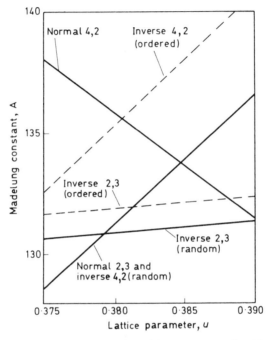

Figure 5.9. Variation of Madelung constant, A, with lattice parameter, u, for normal and inverse spinels

The third factor which influences the cation distribution in spinels is the possibility of a difference in the crystal-field stabilization energies for a transition metal ion in tetrahedral and octahedral environments. The crystal-field strength of the oxide ion is such that most transition elements occurring in spinels are in the high spin state in both tetrahedral and octahedral coordination and the magnitude of the field for the tetrahedral environment is $-\frac{4}{7}$ that of the octahedral. For d^5 ions (Mn^{2+}, Fe^{3+}) and d^{10} ions (Zn^{2+}, Ga^{3+}) there is no stabilization in either configuration. For many other tervalent ions, e.g. Ti^{3+} (d^1), V^{3+} (d^2), Cr^{3+} (d^3) and Mn^{3+}

(d^4) the crystal field dictates a preference for the octahedral co-ordination and this merely reinforces the Madelung tendency of 2,3 spinels containing these ions to be normal $(A^{2+})_t[B_2^{3+}]_oO_4$. However, with divalent ions such as Fe^{2+} (d^6), Co^{2+} (d^7), Ni^{2+} (d^8) and Cu^{2+} (d^9), particularly when they are associated with spherically symmetrical tervalent cations, the additional octahedral field stabilization energy of A^{2+} sometimes overcomes the Madelung factor and results in the divalent ion occupying octahedral sites to produce the inverse structure $(B^{3+})_t[A^{2+}B^{3+}]_oO_4$. With 4,2 spinels, which as we have seen tend to be inverse, $(B^{2+})_t[A^{4+}B^{2+}]_oO_4$, the preference of the foregoing divalent cations for octahedral sites may reverse this tendency and give normal structures $(A^{4+})_t[B_2^{2+}]_oO_4$; thus the only 4,2 spinels known to be normal are $GeFe_2O_4$, $GeCo_2O_4$ and $GeNi_2O_4$ in which both the crystal-field stabilization energy and the small size of Ge^{4+} conspire to outweigh the Madelung preference for inversion.

It should be emphasized that the actual configuration adopted by a given spinel is due to the detailed interplay of a variety of factors such as size, charge, distortion parameter, Madelung energy, the possibility of ordering inverse structures and the influence of crystal field stabilization effects. In all cases the difference in energy between the normal and inverse structures due to these factors is but a small fraction of the total lattice energy of the system and very slight variations may be sufficient to favour one structure rather than the other. The structure of $NiAl_2O_4$ which has already been alluded to is a good example here. Detailed lattice energy calculations of this 2,3 spinel show that the normal configuration $(Ni^{2+})_t[Al^{3+}]_oO_4$ is 25 kcal/mole more stable than the inverse configuration $(Al^{3+})_t[Ni^{2+}Al^{3+}]_oO_4$ if the octahedral sites are randomly occupied and rather less than 25 kcal/mole if the octahedral sites are occupied in an ordered fashion by Ni^{2+} and Al^{3+}. However, the crystal-field stabilization energy of Ni^{2+} in octahedral coordination is some 21 kcal/mole greater than the stabilization in a tetrahedral crystal field and this redresses the balance, making the normal and inverse structures almost equal in energy. As a result the structure is neither normal nor inverse and there is almost complete randomization of all the cations on all the available cation sites.

In circumstances such as these where other effects are neatly balanced it is not surprising to find that polarization (covalency) effects are sometimes the controlling factor. For example, for spherically symmetrical d^5 or d^{10} ions where crystal field effects do not obtrude, the Madelung preference of 2,3 spinels for the normal structure can be reversed by ions such as Fe^{3+}, Ga^{3+} and In^{3+}

which show a distinct preference for tetrahedral sites. For example $MgFe_2O_4$, $MnFe_2O_4$, $MgGa_2O_4$, and $CdIn_2O_4$ are all inverse.

5.3. Valency-disordered Spinel Structures

The preceding section showed that the essential feature of the spinel structure was a unit cell of 32 cubic-close-packed oxide ions, the cation sites being occupiable by many pairs of ions provided that their total charge and size were appropriate. In inverse spinels there was a randomization of the A cations and half the B cations on the octahedral sites. Kordes (1935) showed that randomization could also be achieved by replacing the divalent ion A^{2+} in AB_2O_4 with equal numbers of mono- and tervalent cations of appropriate size. Thus in spinel itself, which can be written $Mg_8Al_{16}O_{32}$, the eight magnesium ions (Mg^{2+}, 0·65 Å) can be replaced by four lithium ions (Li^+, 0·60 Å) and four aluminium ions (Al^{3+}, 0·50 Å) to give $Li_4Al_{20}O_{32}$, i.e. $LiAl_5O_8$. This is a spinel structure with a specific defect such that two-fifths of the aluminium ions occupy tetrahedral sites whilst the remaining three-fifths of the aluminium ions and all the lithium are distributed on the octahedral sites: $(Al_2{}^{3+})_t[Li^+Al_3{}^{3+}]_oO_8$. Other compounds with this valency-disordered spinel structure are $LiGa_5O_8$, $LiFe_5O_8$, and $CuFe_5O_8$. Disordering on the tetrahedral sites is observed in $CuAl_5S_8$, $CuIn_5S_8$, $AgAl_5S_8$ and $AgIn_5S_8$, i.e. $(Cu^+Al^3)_t[Al_4^{3+}]_oS_8$, etc.

A somewhat different type of valency disordering can be achieved if the divalent ion A^{2+} is replaced by a univalent cation; it is then necessary to replace one of the B^{3+} ions by a quadrivalent cation, e.g. $(Li^+)_t[Al^{3+}Ti^{4+}]_oO_4$. A large number of such compounds have been synthesized with lithium occupying the tetrahedral sites and the total charge of $+7$ on the octahedral sites being achieved either by a ($+3$, $+4$) combination of cations (e.g. AlTi, GaTi, CrTi, MnTi, FeTi, RhTi; CrMn, RhMn; CrGe, RhGe) or by a ($+2$, $+5$) combination of cations such as CoSb, ZnSb, CoV, or NiV.

Other more complicated spinel phases arising from valency disordering are $Li_2^+M^{2+}N_3{}^{4+}O_8$ where M^{2+} can be Co, Zn, or Cd and N^{4+} can be Ti or Ge, e.g. $Li_2CoGe_3O_8$. Even more extensive substitution of cations has been achieved in the cubic spinel phases $Li_5^+Zn_8{}^{2+}M_5{}^{3+}Ge_9{}^{4+}O_{36}$ where M^{3+} is Al, Ga, or Fe. The possibilities are clearly limitless.

The disordering of cations on one of the sublattices of the spinel structure, is, of course, not limited to examples in which the cations have different valencies. It is quite possible for a given cation to be progressively substituted by another cation of the same charge and similar size. Normally such cases call for little comment but there is one spinel system of intermediate composition which is particularly interesting, viz., $CuFe_{2-x}Cr_xO_4$. When $x = 0$, the inverse spinel $(Fe^{3+})_t[Cu^{2+}Fe^{3+}]_oO_4$ is obtained but because of the d^9 configuration of the cupric ion there is a large tetragonal distortion of the CuO_6 octahedra, and the phase, instead of being cubic, has tetragonal symmetry with $c/a = 1.06$. When $x = 2$, the normal spinel configuration is adopted $(Cu^{2+})_t[Cr_2^{3+}]_oO_4$ but the phase is again tetragonal since the CuO_4 tetrahedra tend to flatten towards a square planar configuration and c/a is 0.91. Over the range $0.4 < x < 1.4$, the structure is cubic and there is a continuous replacement of Fe^{3+} by Cu^2 in the tetrahedral sites.

Perhaps the most important example of valency disordering among spinels occurs in the compound magnetite, Fe_3O_4, i.e. $Fe^{2+}Fe_2^{3+}O_4$. We have already seen that there is no crystal field stabilization energy for Fe^{3+} (d^5) in either octahedral or tetrahedral coordination but that Fe^{3+} frequently occupies the tetrahedral sites because of covalency effects. This tendency is strongly reinforced by the marked preference of Fe^{2+} (d^6) for octahedral sites since the stabilization in the tetrahedral configuration is less than that in octahedral coordination. This ensures that magnetite is an inverse spinel, $(Fe^{3+})_t[Fe^{2+}Fe^{3+}]_oO_4$.† By contrast Co_3O_4 is expected to be a normal spinel $(Co^{2+})_t[Co_2^{3+}]_oO_4$ because (low spin) Co^{3+} gains more stabilization energy in the octahedral site than Co^{2+} loses by going into the tetrahedral site. Mn_3O_4 is also normal, $(Mn^{2+})_t[Mn_2^{3+}]_oO_4$, but the phase is tetragonal $(c/a = 1.16)$ because of the distortion of the MnO_6 octahedra due to the d^4 configuration of Mn^{3+}.

The significance of the inverse spinel structure for magnetite is that there is a random array of Fe^{2+} and Fe^{3+} ions on equivalent sites in the lattice. This at once explains many of the unusual properties of the magnetic oxide of iron, especially its extraordinarily high electrical conductivity which approaches that of metals. This conduction is not ionic, as in our previous examples, but is electronic; it occurs without migration of ions, the current being carried by a rapid electron-switch process between Fe^{2+} and Fe^{3+} on the octahedral sites. This interpretation has recently been confirmed by the Mössbauer spectrum of Fe_3O_4 which gives one pattern for the Fe^{3+} ions on tetrahedral sites and another pattern

---

† The c.s.f.e. due to the sixth electron in octahedral Fe^{2+} is $4Dq$ and that due to a sixth electron in tetrahedral Fe^{2+} is $\frac{4}{7} \times 6Dq = 3\frac{3}{7}Dq$. The gain in c.f.s.e. in going octahedral is thus $\frac{4}{7}Dq$.

for the Fe^{2+} and Fe^{3+} ions on the octahedral sites; separate spectra are not obtained for the two oxidation states because any one octahedral iron atom changes frequently from one oxidation state to the other during the mean lifetime of the excited ^{57}Fe nucleus, ($\sim 10^{-7}$ sec).[1] When Fe_3O_4 is cooled below $120°K$ it becomes orthorhombic with very little change in cell dimensions or atomic arrangement. Simultaneously there is a rapid decrease in the electrical conductivity, associated with an ordering of the conduction electrons (Fe^{2+} ions) on the octahedral positions. Consistent with this the low-temperature Mössbauer spectrum shows individual contributions from both the Fe^{2+} and Fe^{3+} ions on octahedral sites.

The sensitive dependence of the electrical and magnetic properties of spinel-type compounds on composition, temperature, and detailed ionic arrangement has proved a powerful incentive for the extensive study of these materials in connexion with the solid-state electronics industry. These aspects will be considered in more detail in later chapters. The attention which has been paid to spinel structures, however, should not obscure the fact that randomization of cations on a sublattice can introduce specific defects into almost any regular crystalline array of ions. For example, magnesium oxide has the sodium chloride structure; if the magnesium ions (Mg^{2+} 0·65 Å) are replaced by equal numbers of lithium ions (Li^+ 0·60 Å) and ferric ions (Fe^{3+} 0·64 Å) then a valency-disordered rock salt structure $LiFeO_2$ is obtained. When this is quenched from 700° the cations are randomly arranged on octahedral sites, though ordering apparently occurs on annealing at 600° to give a tetragonal form in which the cations have tetrahedral coordination similar to the ordered zinc blende structure found in $CuFeS_2$ (chalcopyrite). Similarly, the anion sublattice can become disordered in many structures by appropriate substitution and this will be considered further in Section 5.5.2 for the particular case of defect fluorite phases.

5.4. Compounds with Incomplete Lattices

In the examples so far considered of specific defects in stoichiometric crystals all the lattice sites have been occupied but defects have been introduced by disordering the ions on those sites either

[1] Bauminger, R., Cohen, S. G., Marinov, A., Ofer, S. and Segal, E., *Phys. Rev.*, **122** (1961) 1447; *J. phys. Soc. Japan*, **17**, Suppl. B1 (1962) 123; Ito, A., Ono, K. and Ishikawa, Y., *J. phys. Soc. Japan*, **18** (1963) 1465; *J. phys. Soc. Japan*, **17**, Suppl. B1 (1962) 125

by an order–disorder transformation of the whole structure (alloys) or by two or more cations being distributed on sites of the same coordination number in an ionic lattice (spinels, etc.). It is possible to go further and design compounds whose very formula, although stoichiometric, will not enable all the available lattice sites to be occupied. For example, when one mole of manganese dioxide is heated with six moles of magnesium oxide, the compound $MnMg_6O_8$ is produced. This is a defect sodium chloride structure and can be thought of as being derived from eight moles of magnesium oxide by replacing $2Mg^+$ by Mn^{4+} plus a cation vacancy $\square$. The compound should therefore be written as $Mn\square Mg_6O_8$ in which both the Mn^{4+} and the vacancies are ordered in a cubic unit cell having a_0 8·381 Å (cf. a value of $2a_0 = 8·422$ Å for magnesium oxide itself, corresponding to Mg_8O_8). The compound $Pb\square Cu_6O_8$ has a similar structure. Defect spinels with incomplete lattices are also known, for example, $Zn_2Ge_3\square O_8$. This compound can be thought of as being derived from two moles of, say, $ZnGa_2O_4$ by replacing the $4Ga^{3+}$ with $3Ge^{4+}$; this balances the charge, and leaves one vacancy to be distributed in the lattice.

An extensive survey of the many stoichiometric compounds which have specific defect structures arising from incomplete lattices would be inappropriate. However, a few examples from structures with tetrahedral coordination will serve to illustrate how such defect structures can be designed. Two compounds have already been cited during a discussion of the cubic zinc blende structure in Chapter 3, Section 3.4.3, namely $Ga_2\square S_3$ in which two-thirds of the cation sites were occupied, and $Ag_2Hg\square I_4$ in which three-quarters of the cation sites were occupied. Various refinements can be envisaged. In $\alpha\text{-}Ga_2\square S_3$ the two Ga^{3+} ions and the vacancy have an ordered arrangement on the three Zn^{2+} positions they replace in the zinc blende structure; Al_2S_3 and $\beta\text{-}In_2Se_3$ are similar. In $\gamma\text{-}Ga_2\square S_3$ by contrast the cations and vacancies are randomized on the metal sites in zinc blende and Ga_2Se_3, Ga_2Te_3 and In_2Te_3 are similar though the latter two compounds have some superstructure. In $\beta\text{-}Ga_2\square S_3$ there is a random distribution on two-thirds of the cation sites of the hexagonal zinc oxide structure, a configuration also adopted by $\beta\text{-}Al_2S_3$ and Al_2Se_3.

When three-quarters of the cation sites are occupied analogous possibilities obtain: $Hg\square Ga_2Te_4$, like $Ag_2Hg\square I_4$ above, has a defect zinc blende structure, and it is even possible to achieve simultaneous randomization on the fully occupied anion lattice as in $Zn_3\square PI_3$ and $Zn_3\square AsI_3$. More complicated zinc blende structures are $CuIn_2Se_3Br$, $CuIn_2Se_3I$, and $AgIn_2Se_3I$. In the hexagonal zinc oxide series the parent defect structure with three-quarters cation occupancy is $Zn\square Al_2S_4$. Indeed, all compounds AB_2X_4 where A^{2+} is Zn, Cd, or Hg, B^{3+} is Al, Ga or In, and X^{2-} is S, Se, or Te have this structure except $CdIn_2S_4$ and $HgIn_2S_4$ which are spinels, as are most of the corresponding oxides (radius ratio).

Perhaps the most complex defect tetrahedral structures of this type occur when seven-eighths of the cation sites are occupied; these arise when three of the eight M^{2+} are replaced by two M^{3+} and a vacancy as in $Hg_5Ga_2\square Te_8$ and $Hg_5In_2\square Te_8$. These compounds have a disordered zinc blende structure with some superstructure and it is also possible to replace two further Hg^{2+} by $(Ag^+ + In^{3+})$ to give $AgHg_3In_3\square Te_8$.

A particularly important example of a simple compound having an incomplete lattice is γ-Fe_2O_3. The α-form of Fe_2O_3 (haematite) has a slightly distorted hexagonal arrangement of ions in which each Fe^{3+} is octahedrally coordinated by six oxide ions. Due to the tendency of Fe^{3+} to adopt a tetrahedral configuration, the γ-form has a spinel-type structure with a unit cell of 32 oxide ions on a face-centred cubic lattice. In such a structure, as we have seen, there are eight tetrahedral sites and 16 octahedral cation sites available, making 24 positions in all (as in $Fe_{24}O_{32}$, i.e. Fe_3O_4). However, in γ-Fe_2O_3, 32 oxide ions are associated with only $21\frac{1}{3}$ ferric ions so that there are $2\frac{2}{3}$ vacant sites in each unit cell. The structure of γ-Fe_2O_3 can be thought of as being derived from magnetite, $(Fe_8^{3+})_t[Fe_8^{2+}Fe_8^{3+}]_oO_{32}$, by replacing the eight Fe^{2+} ions by the stoichiometric equivalent of $5\frac{1}{3}$ Fe^{3+} plus $2\frac{2}{3}\square$, both combinations having a total cationic charge of +16 units. The essential correctness of this picture of the cation distribution has recently been demonstrated by Mössbauer spectroscopy which has shown that all the tetrahedral sites in γ-Fe_2O_3 are occupied and that the vacancies are distributed on the octahedral sites. The same technique has also established the increase in covalent character of those ferric ions which occupy the tetrahedral sites.[1] A similar defect spinel-type structure with octahedral-site vacancies is adopted by γ-Al_2O_3. The alternative possibility of the $2\frac{2}{3}$ vacant sites occurring in some regular way has been found in β-In_2S_3.[2]

The anion distribution in γ-Fe_2O_3 is, in fact, somewhat more complex than indicated above. It has been recognized for some time that the compound, which is normally prepared by the thermal decomposition of hydrous iron (III) oxides at low temperatures,

[1] Armstrong, R. J., Morrish, A. H. and Savatzky, D. A., *Phys. Lett.*, **23** (1966) 414
[2] Rooymans, C. J. M., *J. inorg. nucl. Chem.*, **11** (1959) 78

can not be made by anhydrous oxidation techniques. The compound always retains 0·5–1 per cent water which appears to be essential for the stability of the structure. Because of this it has been formulated as a phase intermediate between $(Fe_8^{3+})_t[Fe_{13\frac{1}{3}}^{3+}\square_{2\frac{2}{3}}]_oO_{32}$ and $(Fe_8^{3+})_t[Fe_{12}^{3+}\square_4]_o(OH)_4O_{28}$ which corresponds to 2·2 per cent water.[1] The similarity to the valency disordered spinel $LiFe_5O_8$ is obvious: $(Fe_8^{3+})_t[Fe_{12}^{3+}Li_4^+]_oO_{32}$. Further discussion of iron oxide phases will be deferred until Chapter 6. It need merely be noted here that there is nothing unique about the number $21\frac{1}{3}$ which would indicate that the formulae $Fe_{21\frac{1}{3}}O_{32}$ (i.e. Fe_2O_3) should be more stable than, say, $Fe_{22}O_{32}$, i.e. $Fe_{2·06}O_3$. In progressively filling the vacant octahedral sites in Fe_2O_3 it is only necessary to reduce the charge on the appropriate number of ions to Fe^{2+} to preserve electroneutrality. Similarly, in progressively removing some of the octahedral ferrous ions in Fe_3O_4 it is only necessary to use these charges to oxidize some of the remaining ferrous ions to ferric. The possibility of compounds existing as phases of variable composition can thus be seen as a natural development from the existence of stoichiometric compounds with incomplete lattices.

The presence of randomly distributed vacant octahedral sites also explains why substances like spinels can take up indefinitely large amounts of γ-Fe_2O_3 or γ-Al_2O_3 into solid solution. For example, $MgAl_2O_4$ can form a complete range of solid solutions with Al_2O_3; the oxygen builds on to the complete face-centred-cubic oxide-ion lattice and the Al^{3+} gradually replaces the Mg^{2+}, electrical neutrality being achieved simply by leaving one cation site vacant for each $3Mg^{2+}$ replaced by $2Al^{3+}$. As there are eight Mg^{2+} in the unit cell of $MgAl_2O_4$, complete replacement leaves $\frac{8}{3}$, i.e. $2\frac{2}{3}$ vacant sites, as found in γ-Al_2O_3. This example can be seen to be entirely parallel to the case of Fe_3O_4–Fe_2O_3 discussed in the preceding paragraph except that, as Al^{2+} is not stable towards disproportionation, the compound Al_3O_4 is not stable, unless the Al^{2+} is replaced by Mg^{2+}.

5.5. Other Examples of Specific Defects

Three further types of specific defects in stoichiometric crystals will be mentioned because they illustrate additional features of interest.

5.5.1. *Ammonium Trifluorotrioxomolybdate (VI)*

The compound $(NH_4)_3MoO_3F_3$ was one of the first defect

[1] David, I. and Welch, A. J. E., *Trans. Faraday Soc.*, **52** (1956) 1642; Van Oosterhaut, G. W. and Rooijmans, C. J. M., *Nature*, **188** (1958) 44

structures to be recognized.[1] From the pyknometric density and the systematic absences in the Laue patterns, the structure was shown to be face-centred with four molecules in the unit cell. However, there is no arrangement of 4Mo, 12N, 12O, and 12F which is possible on such a lattice or even on an approximately face-centred lattice. If the oxide and fluoride ions could be considered to be crystallographically identical the structure would be the same as for $(NH_4)_3FeF_6$. This implies that the $MoO_3F_3^{3-}$ octahedra are randomly oriented so that either oxygen or fluorine atoms point along the crystallographic axes. The structure can therefore be regarded as having a defect arising either from disorder of an oxide-fluoride sublattice, or from disorder in the orientation of the $MoO_3F_3^{3-}$ octahedral ions.

5.5.2. Silver Iodide

At room temperature the stable form of silver iodide is γ-AgI, which has the cubic zinc blende structure; β-AgI, which has the hexagonal zinc oxide structure, is metastable at room temperature but is the stable form between 136° and 146°. In this structure (p. 51) each iodine is close-packed, being equidistant from twelve other iodide ions, and the silver ions have a similar disposition; this results in a mutual fourfold tetrahedral coordination of the iodine and silver for each other. At 146° β-AgI undergoes a remarkable phase change to α-AgI in which the iodide sublattice changes symmetry but remains rigid, whereas the silver sublattice 'melts'. This has a dramatic effect on several properties of the compound, particularly those relating to the mobility of the silver atoms. The coordination number of iodine by iodine falls from twelve to eight during the transition, the iodide sublattice in α-AgI being body-centred-cubic as shown in *Figure 5.10*. In this structure there are forty-two possible sites for each two silver ions, distributed as follows:[2]

six sites having two iodine nearest neighbours at 2·52 Å;
twelve sites having three iodine nearest neighbours at 2·67 Å;
twenty-four sites having four iodine nearest neighbours at 2·86 Å.

The silver ions are randomly distributed on all these sites thus accounting for their high mobility. The interionic distance of 2·86 Å is close to the value of 2·81 Å found for the low-temperature

[1] Pauling, L., *J. Am. chem. Soc.*, **46** (1924) 2738

[2] Strock, L. W., *Z. phys. Chem.*, **B25** (1934) 441; Hoshino, S., *J. phys. Soc. Japan*, **12** (1957) 315

modification; the values of 2·67 Å and 2·52 Å are 5 per cent and 10 per cent smaller than this, as expected because of the lower coordination numbers (p. 42).

The β → α phase change is attended by an enthalpy change of 1·53 kcal/mole and an entropy change of 3·6 cal/deg/mole. At the

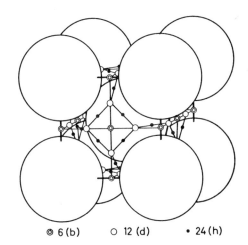

Figure 5.10. Structure of α-AgI showing iodide-ion packing and possible silver ion sites (⊚, ○, and ●)

(From S. Hoshino, *J. phys. Soc. Japan,* 12 (1957) 321, by courtesy of the Physical Society of Japan)

⊚ 6 (b)　　　○ 12 (d)　　　● 24 (h)

transition temperature the β-form has a specific electrical conductivity of $3·4 \times 10^{-4}$ ohm^{-1}cm^2 but the α-form has a conductivity of 1·31 ohm^{-1} cm^2, a value which is similar to that of many molten salts.[1] Moreover, transport experiments show that all the current is carried by the mobile silver ions and self-diffusion measurements confirm that these ions move freely between the easily deformed iodide ions which remain as a rigid framework up to the m.p. 555°.

5.5.3. *Defect Fluorite Structures*

Defect fluorite structures occur extensively among fluorides and oxides and arise from the systematic substitution of either calcium or fluoride ions by other ions of similar size in such a way as to preserve electroneutrality. The structure of calcium fluoride itself has already been described in Chapter 3, Section 3.5.1; it has a cubic unit cell of side $a_0 = 5·463$ Å, containing 4 moles of CaF_2. Some ions of similar radius are:

$$Ca^{2+} \ 0·99, \ Cd^{2+} \ 0·97, \ Na^+ \ 0·95, \ Y^{3+} \ 0·93;$$

$$F^- \ 1·36, \ O^{2-} \ 1·40 \ \text{Å}$$

[1] Tubandt, C. and Lorenz, E., *Z. phys. Chem.,* **87** (1914) 513

Thus β-YOF has a defect structure in which the anions are statistically distributed on the anion sites of a fluorite-type unit of $a_0 = 5\cdot363$ Å. Many other tervalent lanthanide and actinide oxide-fluorides adopt the same structure, e.g. those of La^{3+} ($1\cdot15$ Å), Ce^{3+} ($1\cdot11$ Å), Pr^{3+} ($1\cdot09$ Å), Nd^{3+} ($1\cdot08$ Å), Sm^{3+} ($1\cdot04$ Å), Ho^{3+} ($0\cdot97$ Å), and Pu^{3+} ($1\cdot07$ Å).

β-NaYF$_4$ also has a defect fluorite structure ($a_0 = 5\cdot459$ Å), but here it is the cations which are disordered, the fluoride lattice sites being ideally occupied (except, of course, for the inherent thermodynamic defects which are present in all crystals). Similar structures are adopted by the α forms of $KLaF_4$, $KCeF_4$, Na_2ThF_6, K_2ThF_6, Na_2UF_6 and K_2UF_6 (Th^{4+} $1\cdot01$ Å, U^{4+} $0\cdot97$ Å). Quaternary substitution is also possible in which one of the four Ca^{2+} ions in the unit cell is replaced by a Cd^{2+} ion and two others are replaced by a ($Na^+ + Y^{3+}$) combination to give $NaCaCdYF_8$ ($a_0 = 5\cdot432$ Å), the four cations being randomly distributed.

Further diversification arises when supernumerary anions occupy interstitial positions in the fluorite lattice. This is analogous to the creation of vacant lattice sites discussed in preceding sections but stems from the fact that fluorite phases are more prone to Frenkel than to Schottky defects, as mentioned on p. 72. Thus CaF_2 can take up as much as 45 mole per cent YF_3 into solid solution, the cation sublattice comprising a disordered array of the two ions, the fluoride lattice being complete and the extra fluoride ions occupying interstitial positions (F_i). As an example, when 25 mole per cent YF_3 has been incorporated a_0 is $5\cdot526$ Å and the structure can be written as $(Ca_6Y_2)F_{16}(F_i)_2$ instead of Ca_8F_{16}. Similar behaviour is shown by the systems SrF_2/LaF_3 and CaF_2/ThF_4. It is noteworthy that, although Y^{3+} is 6 per cent smaller than Ca^{2+}, the lattice parameter of the defect phase is about 1 per cent greater than in CaF_2 because of the distortions induced by the interstitial fluoride ions.

A large number of defect fluorite structures in related oxide phases is also known. As previously noted on p. 55 the fluorite structure in oxides is restricted to the largest quadrivalent cations, viz. Zr, Hf and Po, those lanthanides that can be oxidized to the $+4$ state, such as Ce, Pr and Tb and the actinides from Th to Am. Reaction of these quadrivalent metal dioxides with oxides of large tervalent cations such as La and Ce leads to compounds such as $La_2Zr_2O_7\square$ which is a defect fluorite phase with an ordered arrangement of anion vacancies and a random distribution of the cations. When a given element can act both as M^{4+} and M^{3+}, phases of variable composition result, as in the iron oxide system mentioned on p. 105. Thus above 685°, CeO_2 retains the fluorite structure down to a composition $CeO_{1.72}$,[1] one anion vacancy being created for each two Ce^{4+} which are reduced to Ce^{3+}. (At room temperature there are several two-phase regions in this composition range; for example, compositions between CeO_2 and $CeO_{1.8}$ comprise a two-phase mixture of virtually stoichiometric α-CeO_2 and a β-phase of composition near $Ce_{1.81}$, i.e. $Ce_{32}O_{58}$ derived from eight unit cells of CeO_2 by the ordered omission of six oxide ions. The β-phase is thus closely related to the fluorite phase but has a rhombohedral structure arising from a distortion of the cube along its body diagonal.) Likewise PrO_2 and TbO_2 can be reduced to $PrO_{1.72}$ and $TbO_{1.80}$ respectively at high temperatures without change in crystal structure or can exhibit a sequence of two-phase regions. It is noteworthy that, during the re-oxidation of these reduced phases, increasing oxygen content decreases the lattice constant because the added oxide ions merely fill vacant anion sites whereas the cations on oxidation become smaller, and also more highly polarizing. When oxidation is continued beyond the composition MO_2, as in UO_{2+x} the supernumerary oxide ions occupy interstitial positions in the fluorite structure as did the fluoride ions in calcium yttrium fluoride discussed above; however, as the radius of U^{5+} is 10 per cent smaller than the radius of U^{4+}, the oxidation is attended by a continued diminution of the lattice parameter despite the presence of the interstitial oxide ions: a_0 (Å) $= 5.457 - 0.12 x$.

It can be seen in this way that there is only an arbitrary distinction between specific defects in stoichiometric crystals and those occurring in nonstoichiometric phases and the following chapter develops a more systematic account of the occurrence of crystalline phases of variable composition.

References for Further Reading

1. Bradley, A. J., 'Order–Disorder Transformations in Alloys', *Thorpe's Dictionary of Applied Chemistry* (4th edn), Vol. 9, Longmans, Green, London, 1949
2. Green, H. S. and Hurst, C. A., *Order–Disorder Phenomena*, Interscience, New York, 1964
3. Ward, R. W., 'Mixed Metal Oxides', *Prog. inorg. Chem.,* **1** (1959) 465–536
4. Blasse, G., 'Crystal Chemistry and Some Magnetic Properties

[1] Bevan, D. J. M. and Kordis, J., *J. inorg. nucl. Chem.,* **26** (1964) 1509; Bevan, D. J. M., *J. inorg. nucl. Chem.,* **1** (1955) 49

of Mixed Metal Oxides with Spinel Structure', *Philips Res. Rep.,* Suppl. 3 (1964) 1–139.

5. Parthé, E., *Crystal Chemistry of Tetrahedral Structures*, Gordon and Breach, New York, 1964

6

NONSTOICHIOMETRY: STRUCTURAL AND THERMODYNAMIC ASPECTS

THE various stages through which our understanding of the properties of crystalline solids has progressed were outlined in Chapter 1. The concept that a chemical compound must have a rational and constant composition was one of the cornerstones of chemical theory in the post-Dalton period and allowed the satisfactory interpretation and systematization of the rapidly increasing number of covalent compounds being synthesized during the nineteenth century. As applied to molecular species the theory is unexceptionable but it does not necessarily apply to compounds built up from extended assemblies of atoms or ions. A century after the inconclusive Proust–Berthollet controversy (p. 5) Kurnakov showed that many intermetallic or semimetallic compounds had a variable composition and that maxima in melting points, minima in conductivity and other physical criteria did not always correspond to simple rational chemical formulae.[1] This work, like Berthollet's, did not have the impact on chemical thinking that it merited and it was not until the assimilation of the growing body of results on the X-ray crystal structures of ionic solids that the stage was set for the classic paper of Schottky and Wagner[2] on lattice defects and the statistical thermodynamics of real crystals. The theoretical and experimental consequences of the presence of lattice defects in stoichiometric crystals have been examined in Chapters 4 and 5, and it has become increasingly obvious that there is an arbitrary dividing line between defect stoichiometric solids, solids containing varying concentrations or impurity centres or altervalent ions, and nonstoichiometric compounds.

Any systematic treatment of nonstoichiometry must consider the following theoretical aspects:

(a) the mode of incorporation of stoichiometric imbalance in the crystal;

(b) the thermodynamic stability of nonstoichiometric phases;

---

[1] Kurnakov, N. S., Z. anorg. Chem., **88** (1914) 109
[2] Schottky, W. and Wagner, C., Z. phys. Chem., **B11** (1930) 163

(c) the factors influencing the range of composition over which such phases can vary.

The following sections address themselves to these problems. The concluding chapter considers the type of experimental techniques which have been used to investigate nonstoichiometric behaviour, briefly surveys some of the many examples of nonstoichiometric compounds and finally indicates some of their uses and applications.

6.1. Incorporation of Stoichiometric Excess or Deficit

Three methods of incorporating stoichiometric imbalance in a crystalline compound are known: substitutional, interstitial and subtractive. Substitutional incorporation, as its name implies, substitutes some atoms of one component of the compound into the sublattice of the other component; it is related to the order-disorder phenomena discussed on p. 87. Interstitial incorporation places the supernumary atoms or ions on interstitial sites and is a type of unbalanced Frenkel defect (p. 65). Subtractive incorporation achieves a deficit of one component by leaving certain of its lattice sites unoccupied; it can be likened to an unbalanced Schottky defect (p. 64). It is instructive to examine these three possibilities in a little more detail.

If, in a stoichiometric crystal MN a fraction x of the M atoms is replaced by N, then the formula becomes $M_{1-x}N_{1+x}$ as indicated schematically below.

```
M   N   M   N              M   N   M   N

N  (M)  N   M   ------>  N  (N)  N   M

M   N   M   N              M   N   M   N

Formula M₆N₆, i.e. MN        Formula M₅N₇, i.e. MN₁.₄
```

Substitutional incorporation is normally restricted to intermetallic systems where ionic coulomb repulsions are not involved. Indeed, most alloys exist over a range of composition and this range may vary with temperature. For example, β-brass, which is nominally CuZn, is a homogeneous phase which can vary in composition from $CuZn_{0.55}$ to $CuZn_{1.16}$ at room temperature. In some cases the actual range does not encompass the 'ideal' composition, which lies outside the range of homogeneity. Thus, in β-NaPb₃ some of the lead atoms are replaced by sodium and the phase has a composition range from $NaPb_{1.86}$ to $NaPb_{2.70}$. Substitutional incorporation can also occur in predominantly covalent compounds such as the

III–V semiconductors provided that the atomic sizes (r Å) and electronegativities (X) are similar; thus GaSb can take up excess of either component by mutual substitution in the tetrahedral structure (Ga: r 1·25 Å, X 1·82; Sb: r 1·41, X 1·82); the excess or deficit of electrons appears as electrons or positive holes in the conduction band (see p. 164).

Interstitial incorporation occurs when both the cation and the anion sublattices are ideally occupied and in addition some interstitial positions are also filled by one of the components. The defect is analogous to a Frenkel defect except that the interstitial ion is not compensated for by a vacant site. The situation may be represented schematically as follows:

$$
\begin{array}{llllll}
M^+ & X^- & \overline{M^+\ \ X^-} & & M^+ & X^- \\
X^- & M^+ & X^-\ \ M^+ & \longrightarrow & X^-\ \ M^+\ \ X^-\ \ M^+ \\
& & & & & (M) \\
M^+ & X^- & M^+\ \ X^- & & M^+\ \ X^-\ \ M^+\ \ X^-
\end{array}
$$

Formula M_6X_6, i.e. MX   Formula M_6X_5, i.e. $M_{1\cdot2}X$

Such a process clearly results in an increase in the density of the crystal (see p. 152). A familiar example is zinc oxide which turns yellow when heated due to incipient decomposition: a minute fraction of the oxygen evaporates from the lattice while the excess zinc atoms occupy interstitial positions. At 800°C the maximum deviation from stoichiometry is $Zn_{1+x}O$ where $x = 7 \times 10^{-5}$.

Subtractive incorporation occurs when the component in excess has a complete lattice while the deficit component has vacant lattice sites. The defect is analogous to a Schottky defect except that there are not equal numbers of vacant sites in the cation and anion sublattices:

$$
\begin{array}{llllllll}
M^+ & X^- & M^+ & X^- & & M^+ & X^- & M^+ & X^- \\
X^- & (M^+) & X^- & M^+ & \longrightarrow & X^- & \square & X^- & M^+ \\
M^+ & X^- & M^+ & X^- & & M^{2+} & X^- & M^+ & X^-
\end{array}
$$

Formula M_6X_6, i.e. MX   Formula M_5X_6, i.e. $M_{0\cdot83}X$

The formula should be written in such a way as to indicate which lattice is incomplete, i.e. $M_{0\cdot83}X$ (rather than $MX_{1\cdot2}$ which implies complete M^+ and X^- sublattices plus supernumerary X). It follows that, as some cation sites are vacant, the charges on some of the remaining cations must be increased appropriately to preserve

113

I

electrical neutrality. Examples of metal deficit are cuprous oxide, the wüstite phase (ferrous oxide), and the pyrrhotite phase of ferrous sulphide which is sometimes written as Fe_7S_8 but which is a phase of variable composition better written as $Fe_{(1-x)}S$. An example of non-metal deficit is cadmium oxide which, like zinc oxide, loses oxygen when heated; however, as cadmium oxide has the 6:6 sodium chloride structure it can not incorporate Frenkel type defects as can the tetrahedrally coordinated zinc oxide (see p. 72) so it adopts the pseudo-Schottky alternative of vacant oxide sites: CdO_{1-x} where x can rise to 5×10^{-4} at 650°C·

6.2. Thermodynamics of Nonstoichiometric Phases

Any crystal in contact with the vapour of one of its constituents is potentially a nonstoichiometric compound. For true thermodynamic equilibrium, the composition of the solid phase must depend on the concentration (activity) of this constituent in the vapour phase, so that the stoichiometric compound is merely a particular point on the vapour pressure–composition curve which corresponds to that partial pressure at which the number of cations and anions in the solid phase happens to be equal. In the limit of small deviations from stoichiometry the system can be treated by the methods of statistical thermodynamics in the same way as was done for stoichiometric crystals in Chapter 4, Section 4.1. Four main cases arise in the phenomenological description of crystalline ionic phases which vary in composition with the pressure of the ambient vapour and these will be outlined before embarking on the general statistical mechanical description of the system. Two of the cases apply to situations in which there is an excess of the anionic component and two to situations where there is a deficit of this component.

If the pressure (activity) of the gas X_2 in contact with a crystal MX is raised above the value $p(0)$ appropriate to the stoichiometric composition $MX_{1.000}$, then the concentration of X^- within the crystal must also increase to maintain equilibrium. In the limit of small changes in concentration, before phases of differing composition have been nucleated, one of two things can occur:

(a) The excess of anions X^- can go into interstitial positions, an equivalent number of cations M^+ being oxidized to M^{2+} to balance the charge. This can be formulated as a quasi-chemical reaction:

$$\tfrac{1}{2}X_2(g) + e^- \text{ (at surface)} = X_i^-$$
$$M_l^+ = M_l^{2+} + e^-$$

In these equations (g) signifies the gas phase, the subscript i indicates an ion on an interstitial site and the subscript 1 indicates an ion on a normal lattice site proper to the component in question. Pictorially this reaction can be represented as follows:

$$
\begin{array}{cccc}
M^+ & X^- & M^+ & X^- \\
 & & & \\
X^- & M^+ & X^- & M^+
\end{array}
\quad \xrightarrow{X_2(g)} \quad
\begin{array}{cccc}
M^+ & X^- & M^+ & X^- \\
 & & X^- & \\
X^- & M^{2+} & X^- & M^+
\end{array}
$$

This is observed experimentally for certain compounds with the fluorite lattice, e.g.

$$UO_2 + \frac{x}{2}O_2 = UO_{2+x}$$

This variation in stoichiometry is very similar to the behaviour of CaF_2 itself which, as mentioned on p. 108 can take up considerable quantities of YF_3 (or ThF_4) into solid solution to give phases of composition MF_{2+x} where M is Ca^{2+} (0·99 Å) Y^{3+} (0·93 Å) or Th^{4+} (1·01 Å) and the supernumerary ions are in interstitial positions. Formally, the only distinction between nonstoichiometry and impurity solid solution is that, in the former case, the altervalent cation happens to be the same chemical element as the cation of the host compound.

(b) Alternatively, the excess anions X^- build onto the surface of the crystal on normal lattice sites thus creating cation vacancies which diffuse into the crystal; simultaneously, an equivalent number of M^+ on normal lattice sites are oxidized to M^{2+}. Pictorially this can be represented as in the subjoined diagram:

$$
\begin{array}{cccc}
 & & X^- & \square_+ \\
M^+ & X^- & M^+ & X^- \\
 & & & \\
X^- & M^+ & X^- & M^+
\end{array}
\quad \xrightarrow{X_2(g)} \quad
\begin{array}{cccc}
M^{2+} & X^- & M^+ & X^- \\
 & & & \\
X^- & M^+ & X^- & M^+
\end{array}
$$

The corresponding quasi-chemical equations are:

$$\tfrac{1}{2}X_2(g) + e^- \text{ (at surface)} = X_l^{\,-} + \square_+$$
$$M_l^{\,+} = M_l^{\,2+} + e^-$$

where, as before, the subscript l indicates that X^-, M^+ and M^{2+} are all on normal lattice sites, and $\square_+$ represents a vacant cation site. This mode of incorporating anion excess (cation deficit) is more common than the interstitial incorporation of excess anions mentioned in case (a) above. Examples are metal deficit manganous oxide, $Mn_{1-x}O$, ferrous oxide $Fe_{1-x}O$, and cuprous oxide, $Cu_{2-x}O$.

If the pressure of the gas X_2 is reduced below the value $p(0)$ appropriate to the equilibrium existence of the stoichiometric compound $MX_{1.000}$ then two further possibilities arise:

(c) for crystals prone to Schottky defects the anion activity in the solid phase can be reduced by evaporating off some of component X, leaving vacant anion sites and electrons trapped nearby:

$$
\begin{array}{cccc}
M^+ & (X) & M^+ & X^- \\
X^- & M^+ & X^- & M^+
\end{array}
\quad \xrightarrow{-\frac{1}{2}X_2(g)} \quad
\begin{array}{cccc}
M^+ & \square_- & M & X^- \\
X^- & M^+ & X^- & M^+
\end{array}
$$

The corresponding equations are

$$X_l{}^- = \tfrac{1}{2}X_2(g) + \square_- + (\text{trapped } e^-)$$

$$M_l{}^+ + (\text{trapped } e^-) = M_l$$

This mode of incorporating anion deficit is rather uncommon though it may occur in TiO_{1-x} and certain alkali halides. A more usual procedure is the fourth and final case described in the next paragraph.

(d) Both the cation and anion sublattices remain complete (except for the inevitable but balanced concentration of inherent lattice defects) but the reduced cation M goes into an interstitial position:

$$
\begin{array}{cccc}
M^+ & X^- & M^+ & (X) \\
X^- & M^+ & X^- & M^+
\end{array}
\quad \xrightarrow{-\frac{1}{2}X_2(g)} \quad
\begin{array}{ccccc}
M^+ & X^- & & (M) & \\
X^- & M^+ & X^- & M^+ &
\end{array}
$$

It is unnecessary to specify the simultaneous production of a 'cation vacancy' and an 'anion vacancy' at the surface because the balanced production of such 'vacancies' at the surface merely means that the crystal no longer extends to these sites, the surface now occurring before these hypothetical sites are reached. The appropriate equation is

$$M_l{}^+ + X_l{}^- = \tfrac{1}{2}X_2(g) + M_i{}^+ + e^- \ (\text{trapped near } M_i{}^+)$$

An appropriate example is zinc oxide, $Zn_{1+x}O$.

The foregoing reactions imply that addition or removal of X^- ions not only alters the energy of the crystal by an amount equal to the heat of the reaction $(-w_X)$, but also alters the configurational entropy in a way very similar to that outlined for Schottky and Frenkel defects in stoichiometric crystals. Following the same lines of argument, and using the same assumptions and approximations

116

(pp. 65–72) the number of defects created by a given pressure can be calculated. For example, consider a crystal MX in which X is the more volatile component and in which the predominant cation defects are Frenkel-type, i.e. cation vacancies as discussed in case (b) above and interstitial M atoms as discussed in case (d). Then deviations from stoichiometry will occur by addition or removal of X from the crystal and the total number of M atoms (ions) will remain constant: excess of X will cause cation vacancies whereas a deficiency of X will generate interstitial M atoms. Let n_v be the number of vacant cation sites, n_i the number of interstitial cations, N the number of cation lattice sites and N^* the number of interstitial sites per cm^3. For a given crystal structure the ratio, α, of the number of interstitial sites to the number of lattice sites is a constant dependent only on geometrical factors, i.e.

$$\alpha = N^*/N \qquad (1)$$

Furthermore, the stoichiometric excess of X in a crystal of composition MX_{1+x} is given by

$$x = \frac{n_v - n_i}{N} \qquad (2)$$

When there are more vacant cation sites than interstitial cations x is positive; when $n_v = n_i$ then x is zero and the crystal is stoichiometric; when $n_v < n_i$ then x is negative and there is a deficit of X (excess of M). Let $p(0)$ be the pressure of X_2 above the stoichiometric crystal and $p(x)$ the pressure of X_2 above a crystal of composition MX_{1+x}. Then for $n_v \ll N$ and $n_i \ll N^*$, using the arguments of Chapter 4, we can derive the following expressions:
for addition of X^- when $p(x) > p(0)$

$$n_v = N \sqrt{[p(x)]}\, K_X\, e^{-w_v/kT} \qquad (3)$$

for removal of X^- when $p(x) < p(0)$

$$n_i = \frac{N^*}{\sqrt{[p(x)]}\, K_X}\, e^{-w_i/kT} \qquad (4)$$

In these expressions w_v is the energy required to form one cation vacancy, w_i is the energy required to place one cation on an interstitial site, and K_X is the normal partition function of the X^- ion on a normal lattice site and is related to the energy w_X which is evolved when $\frac{1}{2}X_2$ is dissociated, ionized, and placed on a lattice site proper to X^-.

From equation (3) it is clear that the greater the pressure $p(x)$ and the smaller the energy w_v required to create a cation vacancy, the greater will be the number of such vacancies, i.e. the greater the stoichiometric excess of X. Furthermore, for a given pressure a large heat of reaction w_X also favours a large deviation from stoichiometry. On the other hand, equation (4) indicates that the smaller the pressure the greater the number of interstitial excess cations. Likewise deviations from stoichiometry in this direction are favoured by small values of w_X and w_i. It is also worth noting that equations (3) and (4) are consistent with the previously derived formula for the number of Frenkel defects, n_f, in a stoichiometric crystal (p. 70). Thus, multiplying (3) and (4) together gives

$$n_v n_i = NN^* \, e^{-(w_v + w_i)/kT} \tag{5}$$

For a stoichiometric crystal $n_v = n_i = n_f$ and $w_f = w_v + w_i$. Hence

$$n_f = \sqrt{(NN^*)} \, e^{-w_f/2kT} \tag{6}$$

as before.

The next problem is to derive an expression for the pressure required to achieve a given deviation from stoichiometry. To do this it is convenient to introduce a parameter, δ, defined as the intrinsic disorder of the stoichiometric crystal $MX_{1.000}$.

$$\delta = \frac{n_f}{N} \tag{7}$$

From equations (6), (5) and (1)

$$\delta = (\sqrt{\alpha}) \, e^{-(w_v + w_i)/2kT} \tag{8}$$

Similarly, substituting from equations (3) and (4) into equation (2)

$$x = \sqrt{[p(x)]} K_X \, e^{-w_v/kT} - \frac{\alpha}{\sqrt{[p(x)]} K_X} \, e^{-w_i/kT} \tag{9}$$

Multiplying equation (9) by $\sqrt{[p(x)]}$ and re-arranging gives a quadratic equation for $\sqrt{[p(x)]}$ which can be solved by the standard formula:

$$\{\sqrt{[p(x)]}\}^2 K_X \, e^{-w_v/kT} - x\sqrt{[p(x)]} - \frac{\alpha}{K_X} \, e^{-w_i/kT} = 0$$

whence

$$\sqrt{[p(x)]} = \frac{x \pm \sqrt{(x^2 + 4\delta^2)}}{2K_X \, e^{-w_v/kT}} \tag{10}$$

118

As $4\delta^2$ can not be negative, $\sqrt{(x^2 + 4\delta^2)}$ is always greater than x so that one root of equation (10) is positive and the other negative; however, only the positive root has physical significance because the pressure $p(x)$ is a positive quantity, so the spurious negative root can be neglected.

When the pressure of X_2 above the crystal is $p(0)$ the composition is stoichiometric ($x = 0$) and equation (9) yields

$$p(0)K_X^2 = \alpha\, e^{(w_v - w_i)/kT} = \delta^2\, e^{2w_v/kT}$$

Whence

$$\sqrt{[p(0)]} = \frac{\delta}{K_X}\, e^{w_v/kT} \qquad (11)$$

Combining equations (10) and (11) gives the fundamental relation between the equilibrium pressure, deviation from stoichiometric composition, and intrinsic disorder:

$$\sqrt{\left[\frac{p(x)}{p(0)}\right]} = \frac{x + \sqrt{(x^2 + 4\delta^2)}}{2\delta} \qquad (12)$$

The equation is sometimes written

$$\sqrt{\left[\frac{p(x)}{p(0)}\right]} = \frac{x}{2\delta} + \sqrt{\left[\left(\frac{x}{2\delta}\right)^2 + 1\right]} \qquad (12a)$$

or

$$\frac{p(x)}{p(0)} = 1 + \frac{x^2 + x\sqrt{(x^2 + 4\delta^2)}}{2\delta^2} \qquad (12b)$$

Equation (12) is a most important generalization, and shows that the greater the intrinsic disorder, δ, of the stoichiometric crystal the smaller is the relative pressure change which is necessary to produce a given deviation, x, from stoichiometry. Conversely, if δ is very small (i.e. the stoichiometric crystal is well ordered and not extensively subject to inherent lattice defects) then it is very difficult to incorporate significant concentrations of supernumerary ions in the crystal. It follows that, as the intrinsic disorder, δ, must increase with temperature [equation (8)], so also does the ease of forming a nonstoichiometric phase. *Figure 6.1* plots the variation of x with pressure for several values of δ, as given by equation (12) and illustrates graphically these various points. Similar arguments can be used to determine the variation in composition which would ensue if the pressure of component M were varied rather than the pressure of X_2, and similar curves are obtained by plotting the equilibrium pressure of M against x.

It is desirable to state explicitly the assumptions made in deriving the fundamental equations (3), (4) and (12) since some of these assumptions can be removed by more refined treatments (as in Chapter 4 p. 70) and others involve phenomena which form the

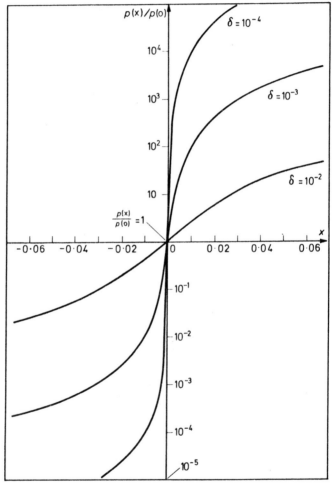

Figure 6.1. Relation between equilibrium pressure and deviations from stoichiometry (x) for various values of the intrinsic disorder (δ) (equation 12)

basis of the factors which limit the range of existence of a non-stoichiometric phase. It transpires that the assumptions in no way affect the principles so far derived or the physical picture of the processes occurring during the formation of a nonstoichiometric phase, at least in the limit of small deviations from stoichiometry. Thus, it has been assumed that the nonstoichiometric defect is confined to one site (a vacancy or an interstitial) though evidence indicates that the parent lattice is distorted over a region of several ions; this means that a number of 'normal lattice ions' near the defect are in special positions both spacially and energetically. It was further assumed that there was no change in the symmetry or dimensions of the parent lattice, i.e. that the nonstoichiometric defects were assumed not to affect the energy states or vibrational modes of the parent crystal as a whole. Likewise, the energy of formation of the nonstoichiometric defect was taken as independent of the number of defects for mathematical simplicity. All these simplifying assumptions can be dealt with in more sophisticated treatments but the broad conclusions remain unaltered. More significantly the clustering or ordering of defects has been ignored. This aggregation or ordering is a necessary part of the mechanism by which a new phase separates and will clearly affect the range of existence of the nonstoichiometric phase; the size-distribution of the clusters and the extent to which aggregation or ordering of defects occurs will depend on enthalpy and entropy effects and will vary with the ambient temperature and the composition of the non-stoichiometric phase. Structural and thermodynamic implications of defect-defect interactions will be examined in the next section after discussion of some preliminary qualitative considerations.

6.3. Range of Composition of Nonstoichiometric Phases

6.3.1. *Preliminary Considerations*

Deviations from ideal stoichiometry involve a change in valency of at least some of the ions in the crystal, usually the cations. In discussing the range of composition over which a nonstoichiometric compound can exist it is necessary to consider the *direction* of the deviation from stoichiometry and its *extent*. It is a general, though not inviolable, rule that deviations occur in the direction of another stable oxidation state of the element concerned. Thus, with cuprous oxide, variation occurs with metal deficit, i.e. towards cupric oxide so that some of the cuprous ions become oxidized to cupric and the formula changes from Cu_2O to $Cu_{2-x}O$. On the other hand, ferric oxide varies slightly on the metal rich side, i.e. towards magnetite Fe_3O_4, so that some ferric ions become reduced to ferrous and the formula changes from Fe_2O_3 to $Fe_{2+x}O_3$. It is instructive to consider these two types of change more closely.

(a) *Deficit of metal*: e.g. $Fe_{1-x}O$, $Fe_{1-x}S$, $Cu_{2-x}O$, $Cu_{2-x}S$, $Pb_{1-x}S$—The presence of a stoichiometric deficit of metal usually involves the presence of some cations whose valency is higher than that of the cations in the stoichiometric compound. For this reason it is normally confined to compounds of the transition metals (and a few other metals such as lead) where variable valency is energetically permissible. If a cation of higher valency is not permissible, then the deviation in the direction of metal deficit is generally negligible. Such deviations can, however, occur to a very limited extent by lowering the valency of the anion, e.g. $O^{2-} \rightarrow O^-$ or $X^- \rightarrow X$ atom. Thus, in potassium iodide under a pressure of iodine vapour, a few parts per million of excess iodine can be incorporated in the lattice at equilibrium. In this instance it is a choice between K^{2+} (involving ionization of the argon octet and an energy expenditure of 730 kcal/mole for the second stage ionization potential of potassium) or iodine atoms, which clearly lower the binding energy of the crystal. It is also possible that cobalt sulphide, $Co^{2+}S_2^{2-}$, which has the pyrites-type structure, incorporates supernumerary sulphur as S_2 molecules on normal S_2^{2-} anion sites.

(b) *Excess metal*: e.g. $Na_{1+x}Cl$, $Zn_{1+x}O$, $Fe_{2+x}O_3$—When excess metal is to be incorporated the hypothetically possible valency changes are reduction in valency of some of the cations or increase in the valency of some of the anions. The latter possibility (e.g. $X^- \rightarrow X^{2-}$ or $O^{2-} \rightarrow O^{3-}$) has never been observed. By contrast, reduction in the oxidation state of a cation can obviously always occur in principle, even if it involves the formation of the uncharged atom. Thus, sodium chloride when heated in sodium vapour can incorporate parts per thousand of atomic sodium in the crystal.

It is apparent that three conditions are necessary for a compound to be stable over a range of composition:

(i) the energy required to produce the defects must not be too large;

(ii) the energy difference between the oxidation states must be reasonably small;

(iii) the sizes of the ions in two oxidation states must be similar if the lattice is to remain moderately undistorted.

These rules indicate whether appreciable deviation from stoichiometry is likely and the direction in which it will occur.

The problem of predicting the precise range of composition over which a nonstoichiometric phase is stable at a given temperature is much more difficult but several intuitive, semiquantitative, chemical generalizations can be made which are consistent with the more rigorous theory. The first of these semiquantitative generalizations is that deviations on the metal-excess side are generally very small and detectable only by the most refined techniques. This is because the presence of interstitial atoms (as distinct from ions) tends to decrease the lattice energy and destabilize the crystal structure considered. An exception arises where the stoichiometric compound has an incomplete lattice (e.g. γ-Fe_2O_3, p. 104) since in such cases metal excess can be incorporated simply by filling vacant lattice sites. By contrast, when the non-metal is in excess (i.e. the metal is deficient), two factors tend to increase the homogeneous range of composition:

(i) increase in cation valency increases the lattice energy of the crystal because of the greater coulombic attraction of the larger charge;

(ii) increase in cation valency diminishes the cation radius so that a statistical distribution of these smaller ions in the crystal results in a progressive shrinking of the lattice parameters; this again increases the cohesive energy of the crystal since ionic attraction is inversely related to interionic distance.

A further intuitive generalization is that the maximum permissible range of composition of a nonstoichiometric phase increases as the electronegativity of the non-metal decreases and as its polarizability increases. Thus, fluorides are much less subject to deviation from ideal stoichiometry than are iodides, and halides have smaller composition ranges than oxides which in turn are frequently less widely variable in composition than sulphides and selenides. This is related to lattice energies of the parent stoichiometric compound, to energies of defect formation, extent of intrinsic disorder, and ease of distortion when incorporating supernumerary interstitials or vacancies.

In considering more closely the factors which limit the overall extent of deviations from stoichiometry it will be convenient to consider first those nonstoichiometric phases which can deviate only slightly from the ideal composition before the system separates into two solid phases. Such systems can be treated fairly adequately by a suitable extension of the statistical theory outlined on pp. 116–119. The treatment of gross deviations from stoichiometry is more complicated and we will find that at least four types of behaviour can be anticipated. There is no sharp division between the two categories and the terms 'small' and 'large' deviations are purely relative, depending not so much on the absolute magnitude of the variation in composition as on such factors as the ambient temperature, the intrinsic disorder of the crystal and the energy of interaction of the defects.

6.3.2. Small Deviations from Stoichiometry

To understand why there should be any limit at all to the range of existence of a nonstoichiometric phase it is necessary to introduce into the treatment so far given terms involving the energy of interaction of pairs of like defects.[1] Let w_{vv} be the energy of interaction between a pair of cation vacancies and w_{ii} the energy of interaction between a pair of interstitial cations. If these energies are negative then the defects exert an attractive force on each other and there is a tendency to form groups or clusters which, if sufficiently large, will nucleate a new phase; that is, there is a critical composition which represents the maximum number of defects the structure can tolerate. If this limit is exceeded the crystal breaks up into two phases (cf. saturation of a solution with a solute). The problem is very similar in many aspects to the critical phenomenon and condensation of gases. Thus it is possible to define critical temperatures in terms of the interaction energies:

$$T_c = -w_{vv}/2k; \qquad T_c^* = -w_{ii}/2k$$

For example, if $-w_{vv}$ is 10 kcal/mole, $T_c \sim 2500°K$ and if $-w_{vv}$ is 2 kcal/mole, $T_c \sim 500°K$.

To compare the theoretical predictions with experiment it is convenient to regard the number of cations as fixed and to vary the number of anions, N_X, all the X ions occupying completely the N_X available anion lattice sites. Then a crystal with n_v cation vacancies and n_i interstitial cations can be regarded as derived from the stoichiometric crystal MX by addition of $(n_v - n_i)$ atoms of X from the gas phase, a corresponding number of electrons being drawn from the cations present thereby increasing their positive charge. Carrying through the normal statistical treatment it is found that equations (3) and (4) on p. 117 become modified by a term involving the energy of interaction of the defects:

$$n_v = (N_X - n_v)\sqrt{[p(x)]}K_X e^{-(w_v + 2\theta_v w_{vv})/kT} \tag{13}$$

$$n_i = \frac{(N_X - n_i)}{\sqrt{[p(x)]}K_X} e^{-(w_i + 2\theta_i w_{ii})/kT} \tag{14}$$

where θ_v is the fraction of M sites vacant $(= n_v/N_X)$ and $\theta_i (= n_i/N_X)$ is

[1] Anderson, J. S., Proc. R. Soc., **A185** (1946) 69

the fraction of interstitial sites occupied by M. Likewise, equation (8) for the intrinsic disorder of the stoichiometric crystal becomes

$$\frac{\delta}{1 - \delta} = e^{-(w_v + w_i + 2\delta w_{vv} + 2\delta w_{ii})/2 \, kT} \tag{15}$$

Carrying through the same analysis as outlined on pp. 118–119 these equations lead to two analogues of equations (12):
For non-metal excess

$$\sqrt{\left[\frac{p(x)}{p(0)}\right]} = \frac{\theta_v}{1 - \theta_v} \cdot \frac{1 - \delta}{\delta} \cdot e^{-(2\delta - 2\theta_v w_{vv})/kT} \tag{16}$$

and for metal excess

$$\sqrt{\left[\frac{p(x)}{p(0)}\right]} = \frac{\theta_i}{1 - \theta_i} \cdot \frac{1 - \delta}{\delta} \cdot e^{-(2\delta - 2\theta_i w_{ii})kT} \tag{17}$$

The form of equations (16) and (17) is such that, above the critical temperature there is just one value of composition corresponding to each pressure over the entire range so that the compound, no matter what its composition, is a single-phase nonstoichiometric compound. This is illustrated by the upper curve in *Figure 6.2.* Below this

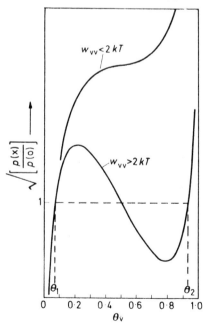

Figure 6.2. Theoretical pressure–composition isotherms calculated according to equation (16) (see text)

temperature, T_c, the pressure is satisfied by three values of the composition (one being metastable and corresponding to a physically unattainable state as with gas condensation). This is illustrated by the lower curve in *Figure 6.2*. The situation becomes clearer in terms of a specific example. Suppose a metal M of variable valency unites with a non-metal X_2 to form two compounds MX and MX_2. Then, if the pressure above MX is raised above the value $p(0)$ appropriate to the stoichiometric compound, X^- builds on to the crystal and an increasing concentration of vacant cation sites (and higher-valent cations) is formed. Above the critical temperature T_c defined by the interaction energy of the vacancies (p. 124), the compound MX and the compound MX_2 (with the same X sub-lattice) are completely miscible. Below T_c, when the concentration of vacant cation sites exceeds a saturation value $(n_v)_{max}$, the lattice breaks up into two phases with limiting defect concentrations corresponding to the compositions MX_{1+x} and MX_{2-y} as indicated in *Figure 6.3*. For a total composition between these saturation

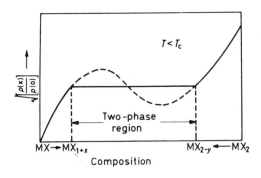

Figure 6.3. Pressure–composition isotherm for nonstoichiometric phases MX and MX_2

limits a two-phase solid system exists with a constant pressure $p(x)$ of the gaseous component X_2, variation in composition being achieved by a variation in the relative amounts of the two phases present. In cases where y is rather small, the pressure $p(x)$ might loosely be called the dissociation pressure of MX_2.

From these considerations it is possible to say qualitatively that the higher the temperature (i.e. the closer one approaches T_c) the greater the possible range of composition of the nonstoichiometric phase. This conclusion is reinforced by a second factor tending to facilitate incorporation of nonstoichiometric excess or deficit, namely that δ, the intrinsic thermodynamic disorder of the ideal stoichiometric compounds $MX_{1.000}$ and $MX_{2.000}$ also increases rapidly with temperature [equation (15)] and the larger δ is the easier it is to incorporate supernumerary atoms or ions—equations (16) and (17). We are thus led to a realization that, on this theory, the range of composition of a nonstoichiometric phase is determined by:

(a) the energy of interaction of the defects, w_{vv} and w_{ii};
(b) the temperature;
(c) the intrinsic disorder δ, which in turn depends on the temperature and on the energy of formation of the defects, w_f.

Four particular cases arise (*Figure 6.4*) depending on the relative magnitude of these factors.

Case (a). δ is negligibly small at the temperature considered; the compounds MX and MX_2 approach the classical stoichiometric

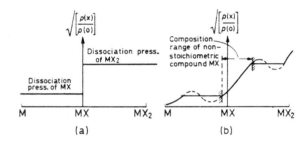

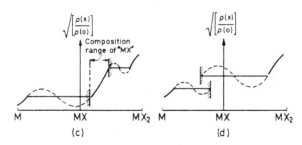

Figure 6.4. Limiting types of pressure–composition diagram

(a) MX is accurately stoichiometric, with zero composition range
(b) MX is nonstoichiometric: δ fairly small:

$$T < T_c; \; -(W_{hh} + W_{ii}) < W_f.$$

(c) MX is unstable, falling in a two-phase region; however, the nonstoichiometric compound $M_{1-x}X$ can exist.
(d) MX is unstable, falling in a two-phase region; no homogeneous crystal of composition anywhere near MX is capable of existence because $-(W_{hh} + W_{ii}) > W_f$

behaviour predicted from the familiar application of the phase rule.*

Case (b). δ is fairly small (the case we have tacitly been assuming); the range of composition is then fixed essentially by the ratio $-w_{hh}/kT$ or $-w_{ii}/kT$ and curves such as those in *Figures 6.3* and *6.4(b)* are obtained.

When the intrinsic disorder of the stoichiometric phase is large, two further possibilities may arise:

Case (c). The intrinsic disorder δ (which is determined by w_f and T) may be greater than the maximum permitted number of defects (which is governed by w_{vv} as well as by w_f and T). In this case (*Figure 6.4(c)*) the ideal composition $MX_{1.000}$ falls within a two-phase region and the hypothetical ideal compound is either meta-stable or non-existent. This is precisely what is observed for $Fe_{1-x}O$, $Fe_{1-x}S$ and $Ti_{1+x}S_2$ for example—the intrinsic disorder of the stoichiometric compounds exceeds the saturation value of permitted defects and a substance of composition $MX_{1.000}$ comprises a two-phase mixture. In the case of $Fe_{1-x}O$ the minimum value of x (0.051 ± 0.002) is virtually independent of temperature between 600 and 1000°C and corresponds to the composition $Fe_{0.949}O$; the maximum value of x increases from 0.065 at 600° to 0.120 at 1000°C thus illustrating the increasing permissible deviation from stoichiometry as the temperature rises.

Case (d). The final case arises if the energy of interaction of the defects is greater than their energy of formation, i.e. w_{vv}, $w_{ii} > -w_f$; then the crystal 'MX', whatever its composition, is incapable of existence as it would tend to unmix spontaneously into two phases (e.g. $Fe_{1-x}O$ below 570°C). This case, illustrated in *Figure 6.4(d)*, arises when the maximum permitted concentration of interstitial atoms is less than the minimum concentration required to coexist with the maximum possible concentration of vacant sites permitted by the value of $-w_{vv}/kT$ in equation (16).

The theory outlined in the preceding five pages has proved a great stimulus to further work aimed at understanding the complex set of factors which influence the extent to which a homogeneous crystalline phase can vary in composition. Of necessity it embraces the

---

* $F + P = C + 2$ where F is the number of degrees of freedom, P is the number of phases and C is the number of components (2 in the present examples). As the gas phase is always present the rule can be rewritten as $F_T + P_s = 2$ where F_T is the number of remaining degrees of freedom at a preselected temperature T and P_s is the number of coexisting solid phases. Thus, when there is one solid (nonstoichiometric) phase at a given temperature, there is one remaining degree of freedom (pressure) whereas if there are two solid phases present there are no disposable degrees of freedom and the pressure is a constant independent of overall composition.

assumptions underlying the statistical approach to the thermodynamics of lattice defects already enumerated. The theory can be improved marginally by taking into account the change in the number of lattice sites and interstices with variation of stoichiometry and this leads to more refined expressions for the relation between pressure, intrinsic defect concentration, and defect interaction energies. A more far-reaching improvement would result if, instead of considering only pairwise interactions of defects, a more sophisticated cluster theory based on a non-random distribution of defects were developed.

In an attempt to remove the restriction that the energies of formation and interaction of defects (w_v, w_i, w_{vv} and w_{ii}) are independent of their concentration, an alternative formulation of the theory has been proposed.[1] This refers the whole system to the parent crystal lattice of the metal M, and derives a succession of phases MX, MX_2 ... etc., by insertion of X atoms into the interstitial sites of the M lattice. X atoms initially enter isolated interstitial sites (type 1 sites) and, by their presence define other interstitial sites adjacent to them (type 2 sites). X atoms entering the interstitial sites at random will distribute themselves statistically between the isolated type 1 sites and the type 2 sites which exist only by virtue of the presence of atoms on the type 1 sites. Similarly, occupation of type 2 sites creates sites of type 3 which are adjacent to two occupied sites, and so on. There is thus a series of energies w_1, w_2, w_3 ... associated with the reaction energy involved in filling the various types of site and also a series of nearest neighbour interaction energies $(w_{ii})_1$, $(w_{ii})_2$ .... These can be used to write down the partition function of the crystal and so build up the complete dissociation pressure–composition diagram for the system.

Both theories are inherently reasonable approximations to the complex reality, particularly in the limit of small deviations from ideal stoichiometry and both indicate the type of phenomena which more sophisticated approaches must encompass. However, both theories involve the unjustified neglect of the interaction between unlike defects. We have already seen (Chapter 4. Section 4.2.3) that lattice vacancies carry virtual charges and that their coulomb interaction energies can amount to as much as 10–20 kcal/mole. This is large when compared to values expected for w_{vv} and w_{ii} and militates against the random disordering of defects required by the statistical theory. A more subtle dilemma is the difficulty of defining what is a normal lattice site and what is an interstitial site in a

[1] Rees, A. L. G., *Trans. Faraday Soc.*, **50** (1954) 335

K

grossly disordered structure. In attempting to resolve these difficulties and, indeed, in trying to see how interactions between like defects could be attractive rather than repulsive as might at first have been imagined, it is necessary to widen the basis of the discussion to include further possibilities for accommodating changes in composition. This wider viewpoint will be elaborated in the following section.

6.3.3. Large Deviations from Stoichiometry

There are two grave difficulties inherent in the concept of a grossly nonstoichiometric compound. The first is the problem of defining precisely the crystal structure since, when a crystal contains a large number of random defects (say > 10 per cent), even so definite a property as crystal symmetry begins to lose its sharpness and it becomes arbitrary to decide which ions are on normal lattice sites and which are interstitial. In terms of a hypothetical example, the two-dimensional array of points in *Figure 6.5* could be described

Figure 6.5. Alternative descriptions of the symmetry in a disordered array of atoms

(After A. L. G. Rees, *Chemistry of the Defect Solid State*, London, Methuen, 1954)

equally well as a primitive rectangular lattice with 25 per cent of the lattice sites vacant, or as a primitive diamond lattice with 25 per cent of the atoms in interstitial sites.[1] This type of behaviour is exemplified by certain transition metal chalcogenides such as nickel telluride which exists over a wide composition range between cubic NiTe and hexagonal $NiTe_2$; the former composition crystallizes in the nickel arsenide-type structure (p. 52) which can take up progressively increasing amounts of non-metal without a phase change until, at the composition $NiTe_2$ the phase has the cadmium iodide-type structure (p. 56).

The second difficulty is that the enthalpy (ΔH) gained in ordering the defects into regular arrays, clusters, or complexes may more than compensate for the concomitant decrease in entropy, particularly at lower temperatures ($\Delta G = \Delta H - T \Delta S$), so that a sequence of ordered intermediate phases may in fact be more stable than a single phase of widely varying composition.

[1] Rees, A. L. G., *Chemistry of the Defect Solid State*, Methuen, London, 1954

For large deviations from stoichiometry, therefore, four possibilities can be envisaged; each is a limiting description and real cases may frequently partake of the characteristics of more than one type, depending on the temperature, magnitude of the interaction energies, packing considerations, etc. The four possibilities will first be listed and then each will be examined in greater detail:

(a) quasi-random homogeneous array of defects;
(b) submicroheterogeneity within a single phase;
(c) intermediate phases based on superlattice ordering of defects;
(d) intermediate phases based on shear structures.

(a) *Quasi-random homogeneous array of defects*—This is essentially the statistical thermodynamical theory already outlined for small deviations from stoichiometry but modified to take account of the attractive interaction of unlike defects, and of the possibility of fluctuating configurations of defect clusters. Such behaviour would be expected when the temperature is sufficiently high for the entropy contribution to the free energy to outweigh the gain in enthalpy which would accompany the ordering of defects and the segregation of a new phase. Examples are the high-temperature phases of 'titanium monoxide' $TiO_{0.64}$–$TiO_{1.27}$ and 'vanadium monoxide' $VO_{0.86}$–$VO_{1.27}$. Thus, above $900°$ titanium monoxide has a defect sodium chloride structure with the extraordinarily high value of 0.155 for δ, the intrinsic disorder of the stoichiometric composition.[1] This means that 15.5 per cent of all normal lattice sites are vacant, implying that less than half of the individual titanium and oxide ions have six nearest neighbours. *Figure 6.6(a)* indicates that for the composition $TiO_{1.00}$ about 35 per cent of the titanium ions have six oxide nearest neighbours, a similar fraction have five oxides and a vacant anion site, and about 15 per cent of the titanium atoms are co-ordinated by four oxides and two anion vacancies. Careful X-ray diffraction and density measurements[1] reveal that the wide range of compositions in the nonstoichiometric TiO_x phase arise from an imbalance in the number of cation and anion vacancies in the structure, *Figure 6.6(b)*, the formal charges on the titanium ions being modified to retain electroneutrality. Thus, at the composition $TiO_{0.86}$, there are 10.5 per cent titanium vacancies and 22.8 per cent oxygen vacancies, whereas at $TiO_{1.2}$ there are 22.0 per cent titanium vacancies and only 6.3 per cent oxygen vacancies.

[1] Straumanis, M. E. and Li, H. W., *Z. anorg. Chem.*, **306** (1960) 143; Andersson, S., Collen, B., Kuylenstierna, U. and Magnéli, A., *Acta chem. scand.*, **11** (1957) 1641

Below 900° the defect sodium chloride structure of TiO_x becomes unstable with respect to a complex mixture of more ordered structures; depending on the overall composition of the mixture this comprises varying amounts of an ordered solution of oxygen in titanium, a low-temperature modification of TiO, a Ti_2O_3-phase and other complex phases which have not been indexed. It is clear that at the lower temperatures, the $T \Delta S$ term is insufficiently large to counteract the enthalpy gain attendant on enhanced ordering.

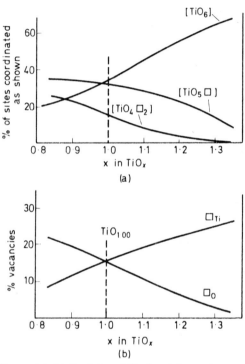

Figure 6.6. (a) Statistics of ideal and incomplete co-ordination of oxygen around titanium for randomly distributed vacancies in the nonstoichiometric TiO phase. (b) Concentration of titanium vacancies, $\square_{Ti}$, and oxygen vacancies, $\square_O$, in TiO_x

(After J. S. Anderson, Liversidge Lecture, Proc. Chem. Soc. (1964) 77)

The stable existence of the nonstoichiometric TiO_x and VO_x phases at high temperatures despite the great loss of Madelung energy resulting from the high concentration of vacant lattice sites may possibly be related to the electronic structure of the transition metals involved. Their behaviour may be contrasted with that of other NaCl-type oxides, for example MgO, which shows no detectable deviation from stoichiometry whatsoever,* and CoO, which has $\delta = 2.9 \times 10^{-3}$ at 1400°C. The crucial distinction between Ti^{2+} or V^{2+} on the one hand, and Co^{2+} on the other, is the spacial extent of their d-orbitals. The lower effective nuclear charge on the earlier transition elements results in more diffuse radial functions, thus enabling the d-orbitals to penetrate from one unit cell into the next; with the later transition elements the d-orbitals are much more contracted and do not effectively overlap with those of neighbouring atoms. For this reason oxides like TiO_x are quasi-metallic, at least some of the d-electron density being delocalized into conduction bands which give added stability to the crystal and provide a source or sink for the electrons involved in the nonstoichiometric behaviour. It may even be that d–d overlap in this sense is assisted by having a proportion of the oxygen sites vacant. A related phenomenon occurs in rutile-type structures where TiO_2 and SnO_2 (with no unpaired d electrons) crystallize in the rutile structure itself whereas the dioxides of $V(d^1)$, $Mo(d^2)$, $W(d^2)$, $Tc(d^3)$ and $Re(d^3)$ crystallize in an orthorhombic modification of this structure in which there are short metal–metal distances indicative of metal–metal bonding. Such anomalies would be expected both for lower-valent early transition metals and for lower valent second and third row transition metals, and even for actinides where the radial functions are also somewhat diffuse. In this sense the metallic conductivity, gross deviation from stoichiometry, and extremely high proportion of vacant sites in TiO_x and VO_x are related to the analogous behaviour of the tungsten bronzes and other bronzes formed by ternary oxides containing titanium, vanadium, niobium and tantalum (p. 177).

(b) *Submicroheterogeneity within a single phase*—An important

* The vanishingly small deviations of MgO stem from the inaccessibility of higher oxidation states of magnesium (thus ruling out metal deficit compositions with vacant lattice sites) and the very high energy which would be required to force Mg^+ or Mg^0 into interstitial sites in the 6-coordinate structure (thus precluding metal-excess deviations). The energy of formation of such unbalanced Frenkel-type defects would be of necessity greater than that of the energy of formation of the preferred Schottky-type defects in this crystal (W_s) which, as we have seen (p. 76) is 90–150 kcal/mole. If W_f is taken to be a 200 kcal/mole, then the concentration of Frenkel defects at 2000°K is $\delta < 10^{-10}$. In terms of the analysis on p.119 this dictates an upper limit to the variation in composition of MgO which is below the limits of detection by experimental techniques and certainly below the accessible limits of purity of the crystal.

new concept was introduced into the description of nonstoichiometric phases by Ariya[1] who pointed out that, within a homogeneous phase, it was possible to have isolated microdomains whose local symmetry approximated that of another crystal structure. These microdomains were too small to act as nuclei for growth of a second phase and did not give rise to superlattice lines in the X-ray patterns because they were distributed randomly throughout the crystal. The submicroheterogeneous structure was considered to be in dynamic equilibrium within the crystal, the regions of differing composition not being rigidly localized within the structure but migrating continuously in the lattice and constantly changing their form and dimensions. The arguments leading to this concept, which were based on enthalpies of formation and magnetic properties of nonstoichiometric phases, are far from conclusive but the concept itself is a particularly valuable one and has undoubted validity in certain systems (see $Fe_{1-x}O$ and UO_{2+x} below). In Ariya's view, titanium and vanadium monoxides $MO_{1.00}$ are to be regarded not as highly defective $M^{2+}O^{2-}$ with equal concentrations of vacant cation sites and vacant anion sites randomly distributed on the sodium chloride lattice, but as a submicroheterogeneous structure based on microdomains which approximate the structures of M_2O_3 and M_2O, i.e. $M^{3+}O_{1.5}$ with one-third of the cation sites in the NaCl structure vacant $(M_2^{3+}\square_+O_3^{2-})$, and $M^+O_{0.5}$ with one-half of the anion sites in the NaCl structure vacant $(M_2^+O^{2-}\square_-)$. Within the microdomains the vacancies and cations are ordered and each microdomain must intermesh with neighbouring units to build up the total volume of the crystal. On the basis of X-ray and pyknometric density measurements this model would suggest that the average size of the microdomains is approximately 200 unit cells $(6a_0)^3$ for $TiO_{1.00}$ and about 1000 unit cells $(10a_0)^3$ for $VO_{1.00}$, though a wide range of continuously fluctuating sizes is envisaged. Such a model for the specific examples of TiO and VO has little advantage over the quasi-random model discussed in the preceding section, and, indeed, the two models become very similar in the limit of small sizes of microdomains or large clusters of partly ordered defects; however, the concept of submicroheterogeneity gives specific form to the clusters and localizes the electrons on specific cations (M^+, M^{3+}) instead of allowing a measure of delocalization through conduction bands. Nevertheless, in other systems the concept has proved extremely fruitful.

[1] Ariya, S. M. and Morozova, M. P., *J. gen. Chem., U.S.S.R.*, **28** (1957) 2647; Ariya, S. M., Morozova, M. P. and Vol'f, E. *Russ. J. inorg. Chem.*, **2** (1957) 13; Ariya, S. M. and Popov, Yu. G., *J. gen. Chem., U.S.S.R.*, **32** (1962) 2054

In the specific example of $Fe_{1-x}O$, neutron diffraction experiments on quenched specimens have given convincing evidence consistent with submicroheterogeneity though agreement has not been reached on the precise structural description of the microdomains themselves. The 'classical' random-defect description of the wüstite phase $Fe_{1-x}O$ implies that the unit cell contains $2x$ ferric ions, x vacant cation sites and $1 - 3x$ ferrous ions statistically distributed on the cation lattice sites (l) throughout the crystal:

$$[(1 - 3x)Fe_l^{2+} + 2xFe_l^{3+} + x\square_+]O_l^{2-}$$

On the quasi-random model it is expected that the ferric ions will tend to complex with the virtual negative charges on the vacant cation sites to form defect pairs $[(Fe_l^{3+}\square_+]$. Ariya considers that the microdomains have the $\alpha\text{-}Fe_2O_3$ structure with all the Fe^{3+} ions octahedrally coordinated. On the other hand, the neutron diffraction results[1] have been interpreted as showing that the ferric ions are not all on octahedral lattice sites but tend to go into the (tetrahedral) interstitial sites, $\triangle$, adjacent to the vacancies thus creating a second cation vacancy:

$$[Fe_l^{3+}\square_+] + \triangle \rightleftharpoons [Fe_i^{3+}(\square_+)_2]$$

This triple defect complex maximizes the attractive energy of interaction between the real and virtual charges on the defects and so contributes to the stabilization of the structure. If such defect complexes begin to aggregate they form microdomains of the spinel structure of Fe_3O_4, the next higher oxide, as can be seen by studying the relationship between NaCl (p. 48) and AB_2O_4 (p. 92). The magnetic properties of $Fe_{1-x}O$ are also consistent with this picture, there being a strong antiferromagnetic interaction between the tetrahedral ferric ion and its octahedral ferrous neighbours.[2] However, there is still need for definitive structural work on non-quenched specimens using temperatures and pressures at which the wüstite phase is stable.

Another example occurs in the oxygen-rich uranium dioxide system.[3] At high temperatures two phases with overlapping composition ranges exist, a 'random' nonstoichiometric phase UO_{2+x} and an oxygen-deficient U_4O_9 phase which can be written $UO_{2.25-y}$.

[1] Roth, W. L., *Acta Cryst.*, **13** (1960) 140

[2] Koch, F. B. and Fine, M. E., *J. appl. Phys.*, **38** (1967) 1470

[3] Roberts, L. E. J., *Q. Rev.*, **15** (1961) 442; *Adv. Chem. Ser.*, No. 39 (1963) 67; Willis, B. T. M., *Proc. R. Soc.*, **A274** (1963) 134

Both phases arise from the insertion of interstitial oxide ions into the fluorite-type structure of UO_2, but each interstitial ion displaces a second oxide ion from a regular anion site to form a defect-complex consisting of two interstitial oxide ions on either side of a vacant anion site: $[(O_i^{2-})_2\square_-]$. This displacement process makes room for the supernumerary oxide ion without too great a geometrical distortion. In U_4O_9 there is one such defect-complex per unit cell, all being oriented so as to build up the large superstructure cell of the complex U_4O_9 structure. In the UO_{2+x} structure the defect complexes are distributed and oriented at random when x is small, but as x increases there is a tendency towards ordering so that the phase partakes of the U_4O_9-type structure. Thermodynamic data on the two phases as a function of composition and temperature show that the entropy of the UO_{2+x}-phase is the higher but that this difference diminishes as x and T increase. At about 1130° the phases are related by a type of order–disorder transition; the 'random' UO_{2+x} phase has the higher entropy but this is considerably less than it would have been for a completely random distribution of positions and orientations of the defect complexes. Thus in a sense, there are submicrodomains of the ordered U_4O_9 structure within the UO_{2+x} phase.

The concept of submicroheterogeneity, implying as it does the existence of small, coherent (though fluctuating) volumes of one structure within the matrix of another structure, raises semantic and conceptual difficulties regarding the definition of a phase. However, the microdomains are not properly considered as separate phases since they mesh coherently into each other at their common boundaries and there is a continuous dynamic fluctuation of their extent and location. Because of this there is an equilibrium situation and the microdomains do not act as nuclei for the growth of a separate phase. There are no two-phase boundaries, but equally, the single phase itself is not homogeneous at the atomic level throughout the whole of its volume. Submicroheterogeneity therefore represents a stable condition intermediate between the classical concepts of a homogeneous solution and a two-phase mixture.

(c) *Intermediate phases based on superlattice ordering of defects*—Early work on nonstoichiometric transition metal oxides and chalcogenides frequently described very wide ranges of existence for the phases studied.[1] Later, more precise work has sometimes confirmed the extensive composition ranges of homogeneous

[1] Anderson, J. S., *Rep. Prog. Chem.*, **43** (1946) 104

disordered nonstoichiometric phases, but in other cases ordered intermediate phases have been detected. Two ways in which these intermediate phases can arise are considered in this section and the next:

(*i*) superlattice ordering of defects;
(*ii*) formation of shear structures.

To understand the conceptual basis for the discussion let us consider first alternative ways of describing some simple crystal structures. When a certain definite fraction of available sites in a lattice is left vacant (e.g. $\frac{1}{2}$, $\frac{1}{3}$, $\frac{1}{4}$ etc.) and when in addition, these vacancies are fully ordered, it is conventional to talk of a new structure distinct from the original one. For example, it was seen in Chapter 4 that a face-centred-cubic array of N metal ions generated $2N$ tetrahedral 'interstitial' sites. If all of these were filled with anions the fluorite structure resulted, but if only half were occupied in a regular and ordered way then the zinc sulphide structure was formed. In this sense it is possible to describe ZnS as a fluorite structure with half the anion sites vacant in an ordered array. If only one-quarter of the anion sites in the CaF_2 structure are left vacant then the C-type rare-earth oxide structure M_2O_3 can be obtained:

$$4M^{IV}O_2 \rightarrow 2M_2{}^{III}O_3 + 2\square_-$$

Because the vacancies are completely ordered, the 'superlattice' unit cell contains eight fluorite-type unit cells (which itself contains $4MO_2$ units) and the regularity makes it convenient to designate the arrangement as a new structural type. The removal of two of the eight oxide ions from each fluorite unit cell ($4MO_2$) reduces the coordination number of the metal from eight to six and the ordering is such that half of the cations have anion vacancies at the ends of a cube-body diagonal whilst the other half have vacancies at the ends of a face diagonal.

Similarly, a face-centred-cubic array of N anions has N octahedral 'interstices' and if these are all occupied, as in MgO, the sodium–chloride type structure is formed; however, if only three-quarters of the anion sites and one-quarter of the cation sites are occupied in a regular fashion the ReO_3 structure is generated (see p. 141 for an illustration of this structure). Because of the simplicity of the new structure it is convenient to designate it as a separate structure-type rather than as a superlattice of the defect sodium chloride structure $M_{\frac{1}{4}}(\square_+)_{\frac{1}{4}}O_{\frac{3}{4}}(\square_-)_{\frac{1}{4}}$.

More complex patterns of occupancy and vacancy are possible and normal spinel AB_2O_4 will suffice as an example. We saw on p. 92 that the unit cell of a normal spinel is based on a face-centred-cubic array of 32 oxide ions, $A_8B_{16}O_{32}$. Since such an array generates 32 possible octahedral cation sites and 64 possible tetrahedral sites, spinel could be described as a structure in which half of the total possible octahedral sites are occupied by B (full occupancy leading to the NaCl structure) and one-eighth of the total possible tetrahedral sites are occupied by A, both in an ordered way. It is the regularity and pattern of this ordering which gives spinel its integrity as a new structural type.

The relevance to grossly nonstoichiometric phases is as follows. If the interstitials, vacancies, and altervalent ions are randomly distributed throughout the basic structure then the phase is properly called nonstoichiometric; but if there is a superlattice ordering of these defects into a new and recognizably regular array, then it is necessary to designate this as a second phase and variation in the overall composition of the system may then arise from an alteration in the relative amounts of the two phases rather than by homogeneous, quasi-random, nonstoichiometric variation within a single phase. The two extreme descriptions are related by an order–disorder type transition. An example of this type of behaviour has already been noted on pp. 108–109 where the high-temperature, nonstoichiometric phase CeO_{2-x}, which has a defect-fluorite structure, breaks up at lower temperatures into a two-phase mixture of CeO_2 and a β-phase $Ce_{32}O_{58}$ derived from eight unit cells of CeO_2 by the ordered omission of six oxide ions. In the case of the praseodymium oxides there is a whole series of these ordered intermediate phases, the geometry of the system defining a homologous series Pr_nO_{2n-2} with $n = 4,7,9,10,11,12$ and ∞.[1] Within each phase there is a small homogeneity range which could validly be called nonstoichiometric behaviour but this is necessarily limited to narrow ranges of composition because the ordering of defects within the framework of one phase soon dictates the emergence of the next homologue. The sequence of ordered intermediate superlattice phases and their ranges of homogeneous nonstoichiometry at various temperatures between 1000° and 400°C are set out in *Table 6.1*. As the experimental determination of x in PrO_x was precise to <0.001 it appears that several phases, notably Pr_6O_{11} and Pr_7O_{12}, have well-established ranges of composition whereas others such as Pr_5O_9 and Pr_9O_{16} have ranges which are appreciably smaller. It is particularly noteworthy

---

[1] Hyde, B. G., Bevan, D. J. M. and Eyring, L., *Phil. Trans. R. Soc.*, **A259** (1966) 583

that PrO_2 itself, which has no detectable range of composition variation at $400°$, shows an increasing tendency at higher temperatures to exist as a disordered nonstoichiometric phase embracing all the intermediate phases down to $PrO_{1.75}$. In other words as the temperature is raised each of the narrow-range ordered intermediate phases disorders into the grossly nonstoichiometric defect-fluorite phase.

Table 6.1
Intermediate phases formed by ordering of defects in the praseodymium-oxygen system

n	Formula Pr_nO_{2n-2}	x in PrO_x	Nonstoichiometric limits of x at $t°$	$t\,°C$
4	Pr_2O_3	1·500	1·500–1·503	1000
7	Pr_7O_{12}	1·714	1·713–1·719	700
9	Pr_9O_{16}	1·778	1·776–1·778	500
10	Pr_5O_9	1·800	1·799–1·801	450
11	$Pr_{11}O_{20}$	1·818	1·817–1·820	430
12	Pr_6O_{11}	1·833	1·831–1·836	400
∞	PrO_2	2·000	1·999–2·000	400
			1·75 –2·00	1000

Another system which was previously thought to be broadly nonstoichiometric but which has more recently been shown to comprise a series of intermediate phases resulting from the super-lattice ordering of defects is chromium sulphide.[1] The system, which is based on the relationship between the nickel-arsenide and cadmium-iodide structures (p. 57) is particularly interesting because it provides examples of disordered nonstoichiometric phases, ordered superlattice intermediate phases and various combinations of these two. Nickel arsenide is an MX structure which permits metal–metal bonding by d-orbital overlap between the transition element ions in the structure and which transforms into the cadmium-iodide structure by the ordered removal of half the metal ions. Various intermediate concentrations of cation vacancies can in principle be accommodated as follows.

(*i*) The vacancies can be randomly distributed throughout the metal sublattice to give disordered nonstoichiometric phases; this is not observed in the chromium sulphide system but is well known in the 'Fe_7S_8' phase above $340°$ and the $Fe_{0.90}S$ phase

[1] Jellinek, F., *Acta Cryst.*, **10** (1957) 620

at 190°C—both phases are metal-deficit defect nickel arsenide structures.

(*ii*) The vacancies can be confined to every second metal layer, perpendicular to the trigonal axis, but be randomly distributed within these layers, e.g. Cr_7S_8 in which one-quarter of the chromium atoms in every second metal layer are randomly removed. The phase can tolerate a slight degree of composition variation, $Cr_{0.88}S$–$Cr_{0.87}S$, and has a CdI_2-type diffraction pattern because of the ordered sequences of layers (absent in type (*i*) above).

(*iii*) The vacancies can be confined to every second metal layer and be ordered within the layers. In order to maintain equivalence of the anions, these ordered structures can maintain trigonal symmetry only for the compositions M_5X_6, M_4X_6, and M_3X_6 (i.e. MX_2, CdI_2-type), e.g. $Cr_{0.85}S$ (Cr_5S_6) and $Cr_{0.69}S$ (Cr_2S_3). In Cr_5S_6 X-ray line intensities indicate that the chromium vacancies are confined to every second metal layer and the presence of super-cell reflections indicates that these are ordered, every third chromium atom in the alternate layers being regularly absent making one in six chromium vacancies in all. In trigonal Cr_2S_3 similar evidence indicates that two-thirds of the chromium atoms in every alternate layer are missing in an ordered way. Because of the stringent geometrical criteria for superlattice formation these phases are truly stoichiometric and show no detectable range of composition variation. There is also a rhombohedral Cr_2S_3 phase ($Cr_{0.67}S$) where the repeat pattern is somewhat larger. The final intermediate phase in the chromium-sulphur system is the monoclinic Cr_3S_4. Here again vacancies are confined to alternate metal layers but, because it is not possible for every second atom in a trigonal array to be missing in a regular pattern and still preserve trigonal symmetry, there is some disordering, the symmetry is lowered, and a small range of composition variation is permitted ($Cr_{0.79}S$–$Cr_{0.76}S$). In this way it can be seen that the nickel arsenide–cadmium iodide structure-system provides examples of broad random nonstoichiometry, and of defect ordering at two levels—segregation of vacancies into alternate layers and ordering of vacancies within the layers. Even when disorder is confined to alternate layers some variation of composition can be tolerated.

(*d*) *Intermediate phases based on shear structures*—Random lattice defects which lead to nonstoichiometry can be effectively removed from a system not only by superlattice ordering as considered in the preceding section, but also by clustering into structurally identifiable groups which are self-eliminating due to the generation of an intermediate phase having a structure different from that of the

140

parent compound. For example ReO_3 has a structure in which MO_6 octahedra are joined by sharing corners as shown in *Figure 6.7*; the rutile structure (TiO_2, p. 55) also consists of MO_6 octahedra but these are linked by sharing edges to give extended chains. In between

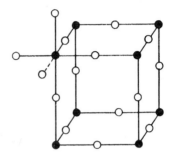

Figure 6.7. ReO_3 structure
● Re   ○ O

these two extremes a whole series of structures can be envisaged of stoichiometry M_nO_{3n-1} in which oxygen is progressively economized (or oxygen vacancies removed) by allowing slabs of corner-linked octahedra to be joined to identical slabs by edge-sharing; the smaller n is the greater the economy of oxygen. This is illustrated schematically in *Figure 6.8*. In reality things are sometimes more complicated than

(a)   (b)

Figure 6.8. (a) Schematic indication of the formation of intermediate phases by crystallographic shearing. One layer of ReO_3 octahedra showing corner sharing of oxygen atoms. If oxygen vacancies (O) are introduced into the structure these will tend to distribute themselves in the configuration shown; the black octahedra can then adopt the positions shown in (b) in which the vacancies have been removed by edge-sharing between adjacent octahedra

(After Wadsley, in Mandelcorn[6])

141

this but a few examples will illustrate this mode of generating intermediate phases to accommodate changes in stoichiometry.[1]

In the substoichiometric molybdenum and tungsten oxides six phases M_nO_{3n-1} have been established in the narrow range $MO_{2.875}$ and $M_{2.929}$ with $n = 8, 9, 10, 11, 12,$ and 14. The phases in the molybdenum–oxygen system itself are summarized in *Table 6.2* and some of the structures are illustrated in *Figures 6.9–6.11*.

Table 6.2
Structural relations between molybdenum oxides

Composition x in MoO_x	Formula	Family	Description
2·000	MoO_2	—	rutile (*Figure 3.8*)
2·750	Mo_4O_{11}	M_nO_{3n-1}	slabs of octahedra connected by tetrahedra, *Figure 6.9*
2·765	$Mo_{17}O_{47}$	'$W_{18}O_{49}$'	complicated linking pattern of octahedra involving 7-coordinate Mo in pentagonal bipyramid, *Figure 6.10*
2·800	Mo_5O_{14}	'$W_{18}O_{49}$'	pentagonal bipyramid sharing five edges with octahedra, *Figure 6.10*
2·875	Mo_8O_{23}	M_nO_{3n-1}	ReO_3-type slabs 8-octahedra thick connected to adjacent slabs by sharing edges
2·889	Mo_9O_{26}	M_nO_{3n-1}	ReO_3-type slabs 9 octahedra thick
	$Mo_{18}O_{52}$	—	MoO_3-type strips connected by tetrahedra and increased edge-sharing at boundaries, *Figure 6.11*
3·000	MoO_3	—	a layer structure*

* Each layer consists of zig-zag rows of octahedra which share edges while rows are mutually connected by shared corners, as in the central part of *Figure 6.11*; successive layers are stacked so that the lowest octahedral corner of one layer lies above the hole formed between four octahedra of the layer below.

It is clear that the possibilities for stoichiometric variation are almost limitless but each individual shear-structure is a well-defined compound of accurately stoichiometric, though complex, formula. Because of the stringent geometrical conditions for the existence of each successive phase practically no stoichiometric variation can be tolerated within a given phase before it transforms into a neighbouring phase thereby eliminating the 'defect'. For example when WO_3 is heated under reduced pressure at $1050–1225°$ the colour changes from yellow to a deep blue-black as the phase $WO_{2.96}$ crystallizes and there is also a crystallographically distinct

[1] Magnéli, A., *Acta chem. scand.*, **2** (1948) 501, 861; Wadsley, A. D., *Adv. Chem. Ser.*, No. 39 (1963) 23; Kihlborg, L., *Adv. Chem. Ser.*, No. 39 (1963) 37; Wadsley, A. D., Chapt. 3 in ref. 6 at end of Chapter

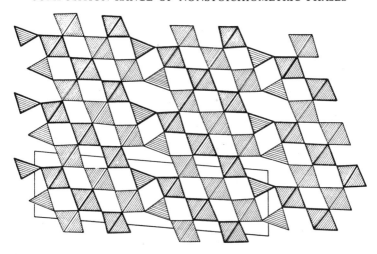

Figure 6.9. Structure of monoclinic Mo_4O_{11}. Lightly and heavily outlined polyhedra are situated at different levels separated by about half the repeat distance
perpendicular to the plane of the paper. ReO_3-type slabs are connected by tetrahedra
across planes lying vertically. The limits of the unit cell are indicated. There is also
an orthorhombic modification of Mo_4O_{11} in which the rows of octahedra in
adjacent slabs, instead of being parallel, are reversed

(From L. Kihlborg in *Adv. Chem. Series* No. 39 (1963), by courtesy of the American Chemical Society)

phase of composition $WO_{2.98}$ which crystallizes as blue-green plates.
The parent structure is evidently unable to tolerate even 0·6 per cent
of oxygen vacancies before shearing to other ordered arrays which
economize on oxygen without leaving vacancies. This is illustrated
in *Figure 6.12* which shows a section of the $W_{50}O_{148}$ structure.
($\alpha - WO_{2.96}$).

As oxygen is progressively removed to give the succession of phases
outlined in the preceding paragraphs, the average oxidation number
of the cations in the structure must necessarily decrease. It was at one
time thought that this occurred by reduction of two M(VI) to M(V)
for each oxygen lost, but the undifferentiated coordination of all the
metal atoms, in conjunction with the electrical and magnetic properties of the crystals now encourages the belief that the supernumerary
electrons enter a conduction band of the host lattice and are neither
localized on individual M atoms nor hop between them.

The formation of intermediate shear phases is not confined to the
oxides of molybdenum and tungsten and an increasing number of
systems are being found which show similar behaviour. Titanium
dioxide (unlike titanium monoxide discussed on p. 131) is the parent

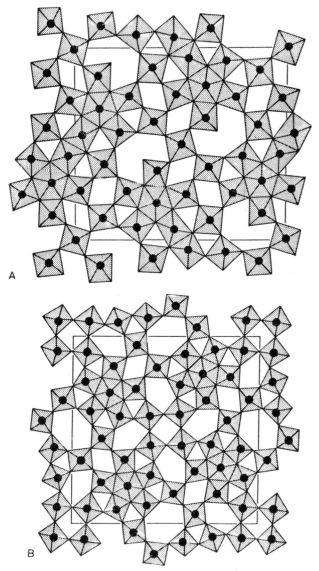

Figure 6.10. Structures of $Mo_{17}O_{47}$ (A) and Mo_5O_{14} (B) containing pentagonal bipyramidal linking units. Identical networks are joined by common apices in vertical array above and below the plane of the diagram

(From L. Kihlborg, in *Adv. Chem. Series*, No. 39 (1963) by courtesy of the American Chemical Society)

144

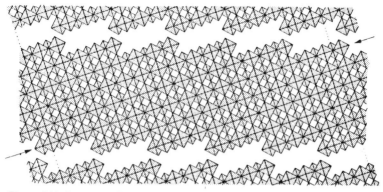

Figure 6.11. Structure of $Mo_{18}O_{52}$. One zig-zag of 36 octahedra, formed by 18 octahedra at each of two levels sharing edges, is indicated by the arrows. 6 octahedra at each end of every zig-zag row share edges with 6 octahedra of a row in the neighbouring strip (separated in the figure, in the direction of the dotted lines, for clarity). Electrostatic repulsion is minimized by moving the Mo atom in the next outermost octahedron at the end of each row across one of the octahedral faces and into a tetrahedral site

(From L. Kihlborg, in *Adv. Chem. Series*, No. 39 (1963) by courtesy of the American Chemical Society)

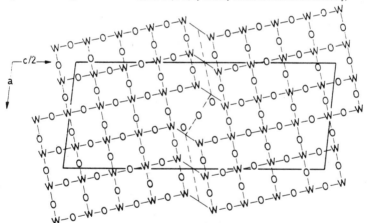

Figure 6.12. Projection of the structure of $W_{50}O_{148}$ (α-$WO_{2.96}$) on the 010 plane

(From E. Gebert and R. J. Ackerman, *Inorg. Chem.* 5 (1966) 139 by courtesy of the American Chemical Society)

for a succession of at least eight stoichiometric phases between $TiO_{2.00}$ and $TiO_{1.75}$; the general formula is Ti_nO_{2n-1} and the geometrical basis for the sequence is the increasing face-sharing of oxygens between TiO_6 octahedra rather than edge and corner-sharing as n, the number of octahedra across one block, diminishes:

n in Ti_nO_{2n-1}	∞	10	9	8	7	6	5	4
x in TiO_x	2·000	1·900	1·889	1·875	1·857	1·833	1·800	1·750

It can be seen, for example, that $TiO_{1.900}$ and $TiO_{1.889}$ are two separate identifiable phases each with its own structural identity. In this connexion it is permissible to draw an analogy between these three-dimensional solid-state phases and a homologous series of hydrocarbons such as C_nH_{2n+2}, e.g. $C_{10}H_{22}$ ($CH_{2.200}$) and C_9H_{20} ($CH_{2.222}$) though, of course the geometrical basis for the variation in stoichiometry is different.

A similar sequence of phases is known in the vanadium–oxygen system V_nO_{2n-1} where n runs from 1 to 8 inclusive: the homologues from V_4O_7 to V_8O_{15} are related to the rutile-like structures just discussed, but the first three members VO, V_2O_3, and V_3O_5 have different structures and VO, as we have seen on p. 131, is markedly nonstoichiometric in the classical sense.

It is not yet clear in detail what factors decide whether a compound will elect (a) to exist over a broad range of composition with a quasi-random distribution of defects, (b) to have domains of submicro-heterogeneity, (c) order its defects into superlattice intermediate phases or (d) eliminate its defects by forming intermediate shear structures. The basic crystal structure of the parent compound is one important consideration since various lattices differ in their propensities for generating intermediate phases by modifying the interconnexions between their structural units. In this sense fluorite lattices with their high coordination number seem particularly adept at superstructure formation by reducing the coordination of increasing fractions of their constituent cations from eight to six. The structural relation between the nickel-arsenide and cadmium-iodide structures and the possibility of transitions between them by ordered (or disordered) occupation of increasing proportions of the interlayer spaces with metal atoms offers an alternative route to ordered intermediate phases. By contrast, the rather open ReO_3-type structure invites attempts to generate more compact structures by the progressive replacement of corner sharing by edge and face sharing of oxygen atoms between octahedra. The ability (or lack of it) to delocalize d-electrons into conduction bands and the consequent formation of metal–metal bonds is also relevant in stabilizing some structures.

146

References for Further Reading

1. Anderson, J. S., *Proc. R. Soc.,* **A185** (1946) 69
2. Anderson, J. S., 'Nonstoichiometric Compounds', *Rep. Prog. Chem.*, **43** (1946) 104
3. Anderson, J. S., 'Some Basic Problems of Solid-State Chemistry', *Proc. Chem. Soc.*, (1964) 166.
4. Rees, A. L. G., *Chemistry of the Defect Solid State*, Methuen, London, 1954
5. 'Nonstoichiometric Compounds', *Adv. Chem. Ser.,* No. 39, 1963
6. Mandelcorn, L. (Ed.), *Nonstoichiometric Compounds*, Academic Press, New York, 1964
7. Libowitz, G. G., 'Nonstoichiometry in Chemical Compounds', *Prog. Solid st. Chem.*, **2** (1965) 216

\

7

EXPERIMENTAL INVESTIGATION OF NONSTOICHIOMETRIC PHASES

IT is manifestly impossible in one chapter to discuss in detail all the techniques which have been used to study nonstoichiometric phases, to review extensively all the nonstoichiometric compounds which have been studied, and to describe all the applications which have developed from their unique properties. Rather it is intended to survey briefly the methods used and the results obtained, relying on the references at the end of the chapter to supply further details and a more complete range of examples. It is hoped in this way to give an overall perspective to the range of phenomena involved and to provide a guide to further reading and study in this area.

7.1. Experimental Methods

Several of the techniques which have already been discussed in connexion with defects in stoichiometric crystals can also be used to study nonstoichiometric compounds. As the principles are the same in both cases it is unnecessary to consider these techniques further. Ionic conduction and self-diffusion were discussed on p. 73, density on pp. 77 and 131 and dielectric polarization and loss on p. 78. Other methods were specific heat measurements (p. 81), nuclear magnetic resonance (p. 82), electron spin resonance (p. 82), Mössbauer spectroscopy (p. 82) and theoretical calculations (p. 83). A further range of techniques becomes available when deviations from stoichiometry occur. It is clear from the preceding chapter that the measurement of ambient pressure as a function of temperature and composition yields extremely significant information and, indeed, pressure measurements, in conjunction with X-ray techniques, have been the most widely used methods for investigating nonstoichiometric phases. In favourable systems such measurements define not only the existence range and thermodynamic properties of the nonstoichiometric phase field but also its structure and the mode of incorporation of the supernumerary atoms. Additional, more detailed information comes from the measurement of neutron diffraction patterns, electronic semiconductivity, magnetic properties, and absorption spectra in the ultraviolet, visible, and infrared regions. Each of these techniques will be considered in turn.

7.1.1. *Pressure–Composition Isotherms*

The phase rule (p. 128) requires that a two-component system with one volatile component is univariant when two solid phases are present and bivariant when there is a single nonstoichiometric phase present at the composition being investigated. The shape of the pressure–composition isotherm therefore immediately reveals whether a solid phase of variable composition is formed. Care must be taken to work at temperatures where the mobility of the ions ensures the attainment of true thermodynamic equilibrium. The minimum temperature at which it is safe to work can be estimated by Tammann's rule, which relates the temperature, T_d, at which diffusion first becomes appreciable, to the absolute m.p., T_m °K

$$\text{for metals} \qquad T_d \simeq 0.33\, T_m$$
$$\text{for salts, oxides, etc.} \qquad T_d \simeq 0.57\, T_m$$
$$\text{for covalent compounds} \quad T_d \simeq 0.90\, T_m$$

Of necessity this is only a rough guide since diffusion does not suddenly start at a given temperature but gradually becomes more pronounced as the number of defects increases and as progressively more atoms have sufficient thermal energy to overcome the activation energy for diffusion. Similarly, the establishment of equilibrium conditions throughout the solid specimen at low temperatures depends to some extent on the time-scale of the experiment and the patience of the investigator. Moreover, structural peculiarities of the compound and the mode of incorporation of its defect may well cause the onset of appreciable diffusion below the Tammann temperature or delay its occurrence to significantly higher temperatures. Nevertheless, in the absence of actual diffusion measurements on a system, the Tammann temperature is a valuable guide to the lower temperature limit of equilibrium experimentation. Thus, for ionic compounds melting at 500°, 1000°, and 1500°C, the Tammann temperatures are 150°, 450°, and 750°C, whereas for compounds melting at 2000°, 2500° and 3000°C, the Tammann temperatures are 1000°, 1300° and 1600°C. In view of the approximate nature of the rule these figures indicate that, for ionic compounds melting between 1000° and 3000°C, caution should be exercised in carrying out equilibrium experiments at temperatures below half the m.p. in °C.

The types of pressure–composition isotherms expected for various types of nonstoichiometric behaviour have already been discussed

L

(p. 127). More detailed thermodynamic data can also be extracted by means of the analysis outlined on p. 124. Pressure of the volatile component can be maintained by direct control of the ambient pressure when this is above about 10^{-3} atm and by relying on gas-phase chemical equilibria below this. For example, by varying the temperature and relative partial pressures of carbon monoxide and dioxide, oxygen pressures in the range 10^{-11}–10^{-21} atm can readily be maintained by the equilibrium:

$$2\,CO_2 = 2\,CO + O_2$$

Pressures can be measured by direct tensiometry using standard techniques such as a mercury manometer, McLeod gauge, Bourdon spoon gauge or quartz spiral manometer. For lower pressures effusion techniques have been used though care must be taken in single-phase regions that the composition is not altered appreciably. A more satisfactory equilibrium technique is to measure the e.m.f. of a solid-state cell; this determines the activity of the volatile component in the solid and hence its pressure in the gas phase. The method depends on having a solid-state ion-transfer bridge to link the two electrode systems and for this purpose 'modified zirconia' is frequently used. This material, which has the composition $Zr_{0.85}\,Ca_{0.15}\,O_{1.85}$, has a conductivity which is independent of oxygen pressure in the range 1–10^{-22} atm and can be used at least in the temperature range 700–1725°C.

As an example,[1] consider the nonstoichiometric uranium dioxide phase UO_{2+x} which has been studied in the range $0.01 \leqslant x \leqslant 0.20$ between 880° and 1080° by means of the cell

$$Fe,\,Fe_{0.95}O\,|\,Zr_{0.85}\,Ca_{0.15}\,O_{1.85}\,|\,UO_{2+x},\,Pt$$

The composition of the wüstite phase $Fe_{0.95}O$ in contact with metallic iron is essentially constant under the conditions employed. The overall cell reaction is

$$1{\cdot}9Fe + \frac{2}{\varepsilon}UO_{2+x+\varepsilon} = 2Fe_{0.95}O + \frac{2}{\varepsilon}UO_{2+x};(\Delta G_1) \qquad (1)$$

This can be considered as the sum of the two partial reactions:

$$1{\cdot}9Fe + O_2 = 2Fe_{0.95}O;(\Delta G_2) \qquad (2)$$

$$\frac{2}{\varepsilon}UO_{2+x+\varepsilon} = \frac{2}{\varepsilon}UO_{2+x} + O_2;(\Delta G_3) \qquad (3)$$

[1] Aronson, S. and Belle, J., *J. chem. Phys.*, **29** (1958) 151

The free energy change in the cell reaction is then

$$\Delta G_1 = \Delta G_2 + \Delta G_3 \tag{4}$$

This free energy change is given by the expression $-nFE$ and, since the overall cell reaction involves four electrons,

$$\Delta G_1 = -4FE$$

where F is the Faraday constant and E is the cell voltage. The quantity ΔG_2 is also known since it is simply twice the standard free energy of formation of the wüstite phase in equilibrium with excess of metallic iron:

$$\Delta G_2 = 2\Delta G^\circ(\mathrm{Fe}_{0.95}\mathrm{O}).$$

Hence, from equation (4), ΔG_3 can be obtained. Inspection of equation (3) shows that

$$\Delta G_3 = \overline{G}_{\mathrm{O}_2},$$

the partial molal free energy of the solution of oxygen in UO_{2+x}. It follows from standard thermodynamic reasoning that

$$\overline{G}_{\mathrm{O}_2} = RT\ln p(\mathrm{O}_2)$$

$$\overline{S}_{\mathrm{O}_2} = -\frac{\partial G_{\mathrm{O}_2}}{\partial T} \; [= (\overline{H}_{\mathrm{O}_2} - \overline{G}_{\mathrm{O}_2})/T]$$

$$\overline{H}_{\mathrm{O}_2} = R\frac{\mathrm{d}\ln p(\mathrm{O}_2)}{\mathrm{d}\,(1/T)} \; [= \overline{G}_{\mathrm{O}_2} + T\overline{S}_{\mathrm{O}_2}]$$

In this way, equilibrium oxygen pressures can be calculated from cell e.m.f.'s, and from the oxygen pressures over a range of temperature (whether measured in this way or otherwise) the various thermodynamic quantities can be obtained. Thus from the oxygen pressures over UO_{2+x} and $\mathrm{U}_4\mathrm{O}_{9-y}$ at various temperatures it was shown that $\mathrm{U}_4\mathrm{O}_{9-y}$ was more highly ordered (lower entropy) than UO_{2+x}, as already mentioned on p. 136. Because of the disproportionation of $\mathrm{U}_4\mathrm{O}_9$ itself at higher temperatures the disordering process

$$\frac{1}{4}\mathrm{U}_4\mathrm{O}_9 = \mathrm{UO}_{2.25}$$

could not be observed directly but, by an appropriate manipulation of the data from the two-phase region, it was shown that $\Delta H = 0.7$ kcal/mole of $\mathrm{UO}_{2.25}$ and $\Delta S = 0.5$ e.u.; these are reasonable values for a disordering process in the solid state. (The calculation involves the determination of ΔH and ΔS for the formation of U_4O_{9-y} according to the equation

$$UO_{2+x} + \frac{1}{2}(0 \cdot 25 - 0 \cdot 25y - x)O_2 = \frac{1}{4}U_4O_{9-y}$$

and then integrating the values of $\overline{H}$ and $\overline{S}$ from $\frac{1}{4}U_4O_{9-y}$ to $\frac{1}{4}U_4O_9$ and extrapolating the results to $x = 0 \cdot 25$.)[1]

Many other examples of the use of these techniques will be found in references 1, 5, and 11 at the end of the chapter. Instead of recording pressure–composition isotherms at a series of temperatures it is sometimes convenient to study temperature composition isobars at a series of pressures. In this technique a recording, vacuum semimicrobalance is used to follow the weight changes (and hence the composition) of a binary compound as its temperature is varied at constant ambient pressure of the volatile component. For example, the results (p. 138) on the succession of nonstoichiometric praseodymium oxide phases were obtained in this way.

7.1.2. X-ray Diffraction and Pyknometric Methods

The principles underlying the use of density determinations to ascertain the type of lattice defect present in stoichiometric compounds have been outlined on p. 77. When two solid phases coexist, variation in overall composition can occur by altering the relative proportions of the two solids and the lattice constant of each will remain unaltered. However, in a single-phase nonstoichiometric region, the cell dimensions alter with composition and thus provide a sensitive means of detecting nonstoichiometry. Deductions can also be made about the mode of incorporation of the stoichiometric imbalance by comparing the observed changes of density with those calculated from the various possible models (p. 108).

One of the first applications of X-ray and density measurements to nonstoichiometric compounds was the classic work of Jette and Foote on the wüstite phase.[2] As the composition moves increasingly away from the formula FeO the composition could be represented as $Fe_{1-x}O$ (implying increasing concentrations of vacant cation sites) or FeO_{1+x} (implying increasing concentrations of interstitial anions). It was found that, on going from $Fe_{0.95}O$ to $Fe_{0.91}O$ the density dropped steadily from 5·728 to 5·613 thus establishing the existence of cation vacancies. The method has since become standard

---

[1] Roberts, L. E. J., Paper number 6 in ref. 1 at the end of this chapter

[2] Jette, E. R. and Foote, F., *J. chem. Phys.*, **1** (1933) 29

and only two further examples will be given: the oxides of lead and the sulphides of titanium.

Decomposition of lead dioxide at 300–350°C yields a monoclinic oxide α-PbO$_{1.57}$ which has no detectable variability in composition and this in turn decomposes to an orthorhombic oxide β-PbO$_{1.41}$.[1] Similarly oxidation of reactive lead monoxide leads at first to a two-phase system PbO–PbO$_{1.4}$ but further oxidation merely alters the composition of the pseudocubic nonstoichiometric oxide, PbO$_{1.40+x}$, the cell dimensions of which decrease from 5·480 Å at PbO$_{1.40}$ to 5·456 Å at PbO$_{1.516}$, as shown in *Figure 7.1*. Tensiometric work confirms the onset of bivariant behaviour at PbO$_{1.41}$

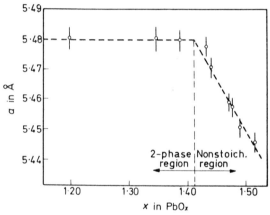

Figure 7.1. Cell dimension–composition relation for pseudocubic β'-PbO$_x$-phase

(From J. S. Anderson and M. Sterns, *J. inorg. nucl. Chem.* 11 (1959) 278, by courtesy of Pergamon Press)

and establishes an upper limit for the nonstoichiometric phase at PbO$_{1.57}$ under 200 atm pressure of oxygen. All these oxides have pseudocubic defect-fluorite structures with varying concentrations of anion vacancies and further analysis of superstructure lines indicates that the α- and β-oxides have ordered vacancies corresponding to the formulae Pb$_{24}$O$_{38}$ ($\square$–)$_{10}$ and Pb$_{24}$O$_{34}$ ($\square$–)$_{14}$ whereas the β'-nonstoichiometric phase has a random array of anion vacancies between these composition limits.

The titanium–sulphur system is an example of the cadmium iodide–nickel arsenide transition which has already been discussed on p. 139. Early work had shown that titanium disulphide has the cadmium iodide structure and that titanium monosulphide has the

[1] Anderson, J. S. and Sterns, M., *J. inorg. nucl. Chem.*, 11 (1959) 272

nickel arsenide structure. However, there was not a continuous variation in composition and continuous transition in structure as in the classic case of the nonstoichiometric $CoTe_2$–$CoTe$ system; rather there were several related intermediate phases each of which was itself non-stoichiometric.[1] At temperatures sufficiently high to establish equilibrium $TiS_{2.00}$ is unstable and the S/Ti ratio is always less than 2·00. For example, for specimens equilibrated at 1000° the closest approach to the ideal formula is $TiS_{1.919}$ and analytical data, in conjunction with the variable X-ray cell dimensions shown on the right-hand side of *Figure 7.2* show that this is the sulphur-rich phase limit of a nonstoichiometric phase extending down to

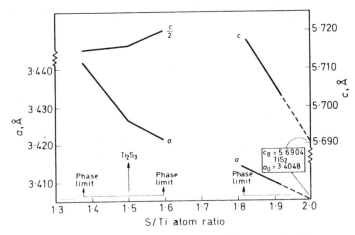

Figure 7.2. Variation in lattice parameters with composition for non-stoichiometric titanium sulphides

$TiS_{1.810}$. When coupled with density measurements these results indicate that the varying S/Ti ratio arises from the insertion of Ti atoms between the adjacent sulphur layers in the CdI_2-type structure, rather than from substitution of Ti for S or the creation of S vacancies. This is illustrated in *Figure 7.3*. The phase is therefore more correctly designated as $Ti_{1.042}S$–$Ti_{1.105}S$. At lower S/Ti ratios the X-ray patterns show that the system enters a two-phase region and this persists down to $TiS_{1.594}$ when a new nonstoichiometric phase field is entered which continues down to $TiS_{1.377}$ and includes

[1] Benard, J. and Jeannin, Y., Paper 17 in ref. 1 at the end of this chapter

the compound Ti_2S_3. There is a marked discontinuity in the variation of lattice parameters with composition at $TiS_{1.50}$ and the sudden appearance of superlattice lines at this composition indicates that the unit-cell is Ti_8S_{12}. On either side of this composition disordering of titanium 'vacancies' and 'interstitials' reduces the unit cell size

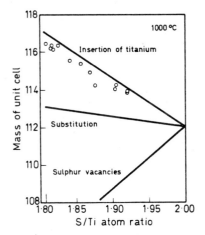

Figure 7.3. Observed and calculated densities for the nonstoichiometric phase $Ti_{1.042}S$–$Ti_{1.105}S$

to $Ti_{2.667 \pm x}S_4$ (i.e. Ti_2S_3) and density data establish that the higher S/Ti ratios up to 1·594 are attained by progressive removal of Ti to a composition of $Ti_{2.509}S_4$ whereas compositions on the other limb down to S/Ti = 1·377 are attained by progressive insertion of Ti as far as the composition $Ti_{2.905}S_4$. At still lower S/Ti ratios a succession of two-phase regions separates three further nonstoichiometric phases each with a narrow range of existence:

$TiS_{1.283}$ — $TiS_{1.305}$ (monoclinic);

$TiS_{1.204}$ — $TiS_{1.333}$ (rhombohedral), and

$TiS_{0.97}$ — $TiS_{1.06}$ (hexagonal, NiAs structure)

The defects responsible for these homogeneity ranges have not yet been determined.[1]

The foregoing examples illustrate the use of X-ray data not only to detect variations in cell dimensions with composition but also to detect the onset of new phases by the appearance of new lines in the diffraction pattern. The precise determination of cell dimensions usually indicates quite definitely whether a nonstoichiometric

[1] Jacquin, Y. and Jeannin, Y., *Compt. rend.*, **256** (1963) 5362

phase is being formed, its range of existence, and the mode of incorporation of the stoichiometric imbalance. By contrast, reliance on the detection of a new phase by the appearance of new lines tends to exaggerate the range of existence of a nonstoichiometric phase because the new X-ray pattern will only become apparent after a sufficient concentration of this new phase has been formed. In the most refined work one examines the density-profile of individual diffraction lines and looks for changes in intensity, line breadth, and line shape to herald the incipient formation of a new phase. The same method has been used to detect concentration gradients within a nonstoichiometric phase during chemical reaction. For example, oxidation of monocrystalline particles of UO_2 below $180°$ sets up a concentration gradient of oxygen interstitials from the surface to the centre of each particle rather than forming an oxidized layer of a new phase around an unreacted core.[1] The calculated line profiles for a K_{α} line on the diffusion-gradient model of UO_{2+x} are shown in *Figure 7.4A*; as x increases the line first develops a high-angle tail and then

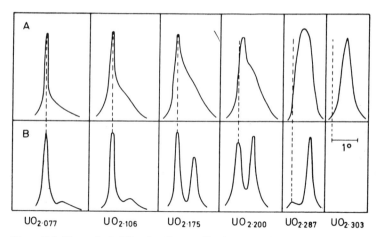

$UO_{2\cdot077}$ $UO_{2\cdot106}$ $UO_{2\cdot175}$ $UO_{2\cdot200}$ $UO_{2\cdot287}$ $UO_{2\cdot303}$

Figure 7.4. Theoretical diffraction line profiles for nonstoichiometric oxides (A), or 2-phase particles (B) of gross compositions marked

(After J. S. Anderson, Australian Atomic Energy Symposium 1958)

finally shifts and narrows as the overall composition approaches the oxidation limit of $UO_{2\cdot33}$. This behaviour, which is the one observed, is quite different from that expected on the two-phase model (*Figure 7.4B*) which predicts the early appearance of a new high-angle

[1] Anderson, J. S., *Proc. Australian Atomic Energy Symp.*, (1958) 588

line which progressively grows in intensity at the expense of the original line.

7.1.3. Neutron Diffraction

Neutrons, like all particles, have associated wave properties and so can be used for diffraction experiments under appropriate experimental conditions. The wavelength, λ, is related to the momentum mv by the equation

$$\lambda = \frac{h}{mv}$$

At room temperature the average thermal energy ($\frac{1}{2}mv^2$) is given by $kT \sim 2\cdot6 \times 10^{-2}$ eV, hence for thermal neutrons $\lambda \sim 1\cdot8$ Å (cf. copper K_α $1\cdot54$ Å). This wavelength is comparable to interatomic distances in crystals and neutron beams have been used increasingly in recent years for crystal diffraction studies. Experimental problems centre around techniques for obtaining collimated beams of monochromatic neutrons of sufficient strength: even with a nuclear reactor and crystal monochromator the most powerful beam of thermal neutrons is only about 10^{-5} times as intense as standard X-ray beams and this necessitates the use of very large crystals (several cm). Consequently neutron diffraction studies usually follow complete X-ray diffraction studies but are frequently able to give valuable new information not obtainable by X-ray techniques. This is because neutrons are scattered by the atomic nuclei themselves whereas X-rays are scattered by the extranuclear electrons. Three effects must be considered:

(a) Potential scattering, in which the nucleus behaves as an impenetrable sphere whose radius, r, increases only slowly with mass, A (r is approximately proportional to $A^{\frac{1}{3}}$); hence the scattered amplitude increases only slowly with atomic number.

(b) Resonance scattering, due to the momentary formation of unstable neutron-nucleus combinations; this tendency varies abruptly from nuclide to nuclide even for isotopes of the same element and may be of opposite phase to the potential scattering, e.g. ^{58}Ni: $+1\cdot44 \times 10^{-12}$ cm, ^{62}Ni: $-0\cdot87 \times 10^{-12}$ cm. Consequently, there may be abrupt changes in scattered amplitude which serve to differentiate elements of similar atomic number and hence similar X-ray scattering power, e.g. V, Cr, Mn, Fe, Co. Furthermore light elements such as H, C, N, O frequently have a scattering power which is comparable to or even greater than that of much heavier elements. These various effects are illustrated in Table 7.1.

157

(c) The third factor which influences the scattering amplitude is magnetic scattering due to the interaction of the magnetic dipole of the neutron with unpaired electron spins on atoms within the crystal. In this way the 'magnetic structure' of a compound can be studied in addition to its crystal structure.

Table 7.1

Neutron scattering amplitude (b) of typical elements (for natural isotopic constitution)

Light elements		Consecutive transition elements		Heavy elements	
Element	$b(10^{-12}$ cm$)$	*Element*	$b(10^{-12}$ cm$)$	*Element*	$b(10^{-12}$ cm$)$
^{1}H	-0.378	V	-0.05	Mo	0.661
^{2}D	0.65	Cr	0.352	W	0.466
Be	0.774	Mn	-0.36	Pd	0.59
C	0.661	Fe	0.96	Pb	0.96
N	0.940	Co	0.25	Hf	0.88
O	0.577	Ni	1.03	U	0.85

The foregoing distinctions between neutron and X-ray diffraction define the unique contributions which neutron diffraction can make to the study of defect solid phases and nonstoichiometric compounds. The location of hydrogen (or deuterium) atoms in nonstoichiometric metal hydrides has provided invaluable information additional to that obtained by tensiometric and X-ray diffraction techniques; these latter techniques reveal the presence of successive phases as hydrogen is added and can precisely locate the position of the metal atoms but are unable to define the actual sites occupied by the hydrogen atoms*. Neutron diffraction studies have shown, for example, that titanium, zirconium, and hafnium each form a single-phase nonstoichiometric hydride of defect-fluorite structure in which there are vacant anion sites, e.g. $HfD_{1.62}$–$HfD_{1.82}$. When a certain fraction of the anion sites have been filled there is a slight distortion to a face-centred tetragonal structure which is also nonstoichiometric, e.g. $HfD_{1.82}$–$HfD_{1.98}$. It is interesting to note that, unlike the oxide systems previously discussed, the cell dimensions of these hafnium hydride phases are independent of composition within each phase.

The palladium–hydrogen system affords another example of the use of neutron diffraction to locate light atoms in the presence of

---

* Scattering intensity is proportional to the square of the scattering amplitude. Hence the X-ray scattering power of hydrogen compared to, say, hafnium is $Z_H^2/Z_{Hf}^2 = 1/5184$ whereas for neutrons the relative scattering power is $b_H^2/b_{Hf}^2 = 1/5.42$. For deuterium and hafnium the relative neutron scattering power is $1/1.83$.

heavy atoms, the ratio of scattering intensities being 1/2116 for X-rays, 1/2·44 for neutrons, and 1/0·824 using deuterium instead of hydrogen in the neutron-diffraction experiments. Thus it was shown that there are two nonstoichiometric face-centred cubic phases: an α-phase at very low hydrogen concentrations and a β-phase which reaches a saturation limit of $PdH_{0.7}$ at normal temperatures and pressures. In the β-phase the hydrogen atoms are randomly distributed on the octahedral sites forming essentially a defect sodium-chloride-type structure with 30 per cent or more of the 'anion' sites vacant.

Similarly, the precise determination of oxygen positions in heavy metal binary and ternary oxide phases has greatly enhanced the value of X-ray results which frequently only locate the metal atoms. For example, neutron diffraction work on U_3O_8 led to a correction of the oxygen positions which had been proposed on the basis of X-ray diffraction and favoured the conclusion that the unit cell contained two U^{5+} and one U^{6+} in agreement with magnetic data, rather than one U^{4+} and two U^{6+} as deduced from the X-ray structure. In UO_{2+b}, as we have already seen (p. 136), there are oxygen interstitials in a fluorite-type lattice. Neutron diffraction intensities are consistent with the belief that these supernumerary oxygens are distributed randomly on the interstitial sites present at $\frac{1}{2}\frac{1}{2}\frac{1}{2}$, $\frac{1}{2}00$, $0\frac{1}{2}0$, and $00\frac{1}{2}$ as indicated in *Figure 7.5*. At the same time, in order

Figure 7.5. The fluorite unit cell of uranium dioxide. There are inter-stitial sites at $\frac{1}{2}\frac{1}{2}\frac{1}{2}$ (marked by a triangle) at $\frac{1}{2}00$, $0\frac{1}{2}0$ and $00\frac{1}{2}$, (see *Figure 3.7*). At the composition $UO_{2.1}$ the excess oxygen is in-corporated on some of these inter-stitial sites and the 'normal' oxygen atoms are displaced outwards to accommodate them, as indicated by the arrows

(After Bacon[2])

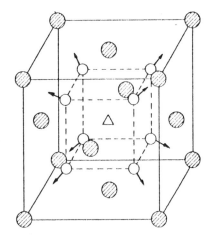

$\bigotimes$ U, $\bigcirc$ 0, $\triangle$ Interstitial oxygen site

to minimize the strain around the interstitial oxygen, there is a displacement of the surrounding oxide ions on normal lattice sites from positions such as $\frac{1}{4}\frac{1}{4}\frac{1}{4}$ to about $\frac{1}{5}\frac{1}{5}\frac{1}{5}$. Likewise the large scattering amplitude for oxygen (see *Table 7.1*) enables the oxygen parameter *u* in spinels to be determined very accurately (see *Table 5.1*).

The inverse of the detection of light atoms in the presence of heavy atoms is the use of neutron diffraction to distinguish clearly between elements of very similar atomic number which are almost indistinguishable by means of X-ray diffraction. Thus, the appreciable difference in both the amplitude and phase of neutron scattering by nickel and manganese (*Table 7.1*) has permitted the detection of superlattice ordering in Ni_3Mn whereas the closely similar X-ray scattering power of the two elements obscures this effect. Similarly in the spinel $MgAl_2O_4$, neutron diffraction clearly distinguishes magnesium $(Z = 12)$ from aluminium $(Z = 13)$ and shows the compound to have the normal configuration. On the other hand, for $MnFe_2O_4$ it was found that only 80 per cent of the A sites were occupied by Mn, i.e. $\lambda = 0.1$ in *Table 5.1*.

The use of neutron diffraction to elucidate the magnetic and crystal structure of the wüstite phase has already been discussed on p. 135 and the method has now become a standard technique for investigating the magnetic ordering in ferrites and other magnetic phases. The classic example is magnetite, Fe_3O_4 (p. 101): X-ray diffraction techniques are quite unable to distinguish between Fe^{2+} and Fe^{3+} but the neutron scattering amplitudes (b) of these two ions are quite different because of their differing spins and magnetic moments $(Fe^{2+}$: four unpaired electrons, $b = 1.09 \times 10^{-12}$ cm; Fe^{3+}: five unpaired electrons, $b = 1.36 \times 10^{-12}$ cm). Neutron diffraction revealed experimentally for the first time that magnetite had the inverse spinel structure $(Fe^{3+})_A[Fe^{2+}Fe^{3+}]_BO_4$ and established further that the magnetic moments of ions on the A sites were aligned antiparallel to those on the B sites; the moments of the two sets of ferric ions therefore cancel leaving a resultant magnetic moment equivalent to one Fe^{2+} ion per formula weight in complete agreement with Néel's theory of ferrimagnetism.

7.1.4. Electron Diffraction

The wave nature of electrons, as with neutrons, can be exploited by means of diffraction techniques. An electron of mass *m* and charge *e* accelerated by a potential V has an energy eV and a velocity given by

$$eV = \tfrac{1}{2}mv^2$$

Hence $v = (2eV/m)^{\frac{1}{2}}$ and, as $\lambda = h/(mv)$ we have $\lambda = h/\sqrt{(2meV)}$ For 40 kV electrons $\lambda \sim 0.06$ Å which is rather shorter than typical X-ray or thermal-neutron wavelengths but is still usable for crystal diffraction work. The limitation of electron diffraction is precisely the opposite of that for neutron diffraction, namely that the penetrating power of electrons is extremely small. For example a 50 kV electron beam can penetrate only about 100 atomic layers before the energy is completely dissipated by inelastic scattering. However, the elastic scattering efficiency is some 10^7 times greater than that of X-rays. These two properties of electron beams, their small penetrating power and high scattering efficiency make electron diffraction an ideal technique for studying lattice defects in crystal surfaces, thin films, and nonstoichiometric surface oxides. Electron diffraction is also more powerful than X-ray diffraction in locating light atoms such as carbon, nitrogen and oxygen in the presence of heavy atoms. However, the technique is not generally applicable to the study of defects in bulk phases.

7.1.5. Electronic Semiconductivity

Electrical conduction in ionic solids can arise either from ionic migration or from electronic semiconduction. Ionic migration has already been discussed (p. 73) and the present section outlines the electronic properties of defect solid phases with particular emphasis on nonstoichiometric compounds. When a set of N atoms or ions is condensed from the gas phase to form a crystalline solid the discrete electronic energy levels of the individual atoms interact and spread into bands of allowed energy separated by forbidden energy gaps. Each band can accommodate $2nN$ electrons where n is the degeneracy of the originating atomic energy level. The band structure of the electronic energy levels of solids is a consequence of the Pauli exclusion principle and the precise form of the bands can be deduced by solving the total Schrödinger equation for the system using a periodically varying potential function having the periodicity of the crystal lattice, rather than the more familiar central-force-field potential appropriate to individual atoms.

For pure, accurately stoichiometric compounds three limiting cases arise as illustrated schematically in *Figure 7.6*. Some solids are electrical insulators (e.g. pure MgO); for these, each occupied band is exactly filled with its quota of electrons and there is a large forbidden energy gap ΔE_0 to the next allowed level which is thus completely empty (*Figure 7.6a*). For magnesium oxide ΔE_0 is 170 kcal/mole, for alkali metal chlorides, bromides, and iodides it is between 160 and 230 kcal/mole and for alkali metal fluorides the gap increases to as much as 280 kcal/mole. Under these conditions electrons in the filled bands are unable to accept slight increments of energy under an applied electric field and there is no mechanism for conducting electric current through the solid except by complete dielectric breakdown at extremely high voltages.

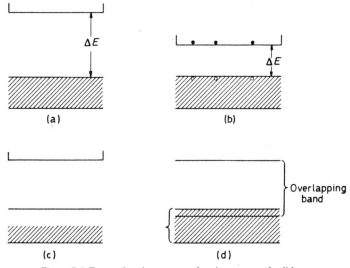

Figure 7.6. Energy band structure of various types of solid

(a) insulator; $\Delta E \gg kT$; (b) intrinsic semiconductor; $\Delta E \sim kT$; (c) metal: highest occupied band only partly filled; (d) metal: two overlapping bands leading to immediately accessible energy levels

The second case for pure compounds is when the forbidden energy gap is within an order of magnitude of thermally accessible energies ($N_0 kT = \boldsymbol{R}T \sim 0.6$ kcal/mole at room temperature and 2.15 kcal/mole at 800°C). Such compounds are insulators at low temperatures but, as the temperature is raised, increasing numbers of electrons are promoted from the filled band into the conduction band and the compound becomes a semiconductor with a conductivity which increases exponentially with temperature (*Figure 7.6b*). Both the electrons in the conduction band and the positive holes in the almost filled band contribute to this conductivity. A positive hole is a place in the energy band from which an electron is missing and should not be confused with a vacant lattice site which is a place in the crystal from which an atom is missing. As expected from trends in atomic energy levels, the magnitude of the gap ΔE_0 diminishes with increasing atomic number. Some typical values are given in the second column of *Table 7.2*. The rapid decrease in ΔE_0 for the

162

Group IV elements is particularly marked, falling from 115 kcal/mole for carbon to 1·8 kcal/mole for grey tin and zero for white (metallic) tin, and lead. There is also a trend to smaller values in an isoelectronic series as ionic bonding diminishes and covalency increases, e.g. AgI(65), CdTe(37), InSb(5·8), grey Sn(1·8 kcal/mole). It should perhaps be emphasized that there is only an arbitrary distinction between insulators and semiconductors, there being a continual variation in energy gap from several hundred kilocalories to fractions of a kilocalorie.

Table 7.2

Energy gaps and carrier mobilities for some intrinsic and impurity semiconductors

Element or Compound	ΔE_0 (kcal/mole)	ΔE_n (kcal/mole)	ΔE_p (kcal/mole)	$v_n(25°)$ (cm^{2}V^{-1}sec^{-1})	$v_p(25°)$ (cm^{2}V^{-1}sec^{-1})
Diamond	115		6·9	1800	1300
Si	27·9	0·7–1·6	1·2–3·7	1300	500
Ge	18·1	0·2–0·3	0·2–0·3	4500	3500
Sn(grey)	1·8			2500	2400
GaP	55				20
GaAs	37			600	400
GaSb	18			5000	1000
InP	30			4600	100
InAs	10·4			30000	250
InSb	5·8		0·18(Zn, Cd)	80000	1400
ZnS	88	5·8(Zn)	23(S)		
ZnSe	65	5·8(Zn)	14(Se)		
ZnTe	20	5·8(Zn)	7(Te)		
CdS	55	0·7(Cd)	23(S)	210	
CdSe	43	0·7(Cd)	14(Se)	100	
CdTe	37	0·7(Cd)	7(Te)	950	90
(MgO)	(170)				~2
ZnO	74	1·2(Zn)		150–200	
CdO	53			20	

The third limiting case describes the situation in metals: here either the highest occupied band is only partly filled with electrons (e.g. Na, in which there are N $3s$ electrons in a band which can accommodate $2N$ electrons, *Figure 7.6c*), or two bands overlap, allowing electrons from an otherwise full band to 'leak over' into the next higher band (e.g. Mg, in which there are $2N$ $3s$ electrons, but the $3s$

band is overlapped by the *3p* band which can itself hold a further
$6N$ electrons, *Figure 7.6d*). In both instances there are levels immediately adjacent to the highest occupied levels to which electrons
can move under the influence of an applied potential and the metal
is a good electronic conductor.

Nonstoichiometric compounds and impurity-doped crystals offer
an alternative mechanism for semiconduction in solids. Impurity
semiconductors (which include nonstoichiometric compounds) are
insulators at low temperature but have discrete impurity levels between the highest filled band and the conduction band which can act
either as a source or sink for electrons. The impurity levels are discrete rather than connected into a band because they are normally
sufficiently dilute to prevent extensive mutual and cooperative
interaction. Two cases arise:

(*a*) excess or n-type semiconductors, e.g. nonstoichiometric zinc
   oxide with an excess of zinc, $Zn_{1+x}O$;
(*b*) deficit or p-type semiconductors, e.g. nonstoichiometric cuprous
   oxide with a deficit of metal $Cu_{2-x}O$.

The band picture of an n-type semiconductor is shown in *Figure
7.7*. Electron donor levels exist at a distance ΔE_n below the conduction band. As the temperature is raised increasing numbers of electrons are excited thermally from the impurity levels into the conduction band and the conductivity, κ, rises

$$\kappa = \text{const. } e^{-\Delta E_n/RT}$$

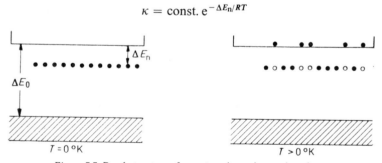

Figure 7.7. Band structure of an n-type impurity semiconductor

Hence an activation energy plot of log κ against $1/T$ gives the energy
separation ΔE_n. We saw on p. 116 that nonstoichiometric zinc oxide
contained interstitial zinc ions on which electrons were trapped to
give zinc atoms, and perhaps some Zn^+ ions. It is these zinc atoms
which act as the donor impurity levels and from which electrons

can be promoted into the conduction band of the crystal either thermally or by irradiation with light of appropriate wavelength (photoconduction). *Table 7.2* shows that the energy gap ΔE_n is only 1·2 kcal/mole for nonstoichiometric zinc oxide and this is much less than the intrinsic energy gap $\Delta E_o = 74$ kcal/mole. Moreover there is a dynamic equilibrium which relates the number of interstitials with the ambient pressure (p. 117) so that the magnitude of the conductivity at a given temperature is a sensitive indicator of the extent of the deviation from stoichiometry.

Deficit or p-type semiconductors also have impurity levels between the highest-filled band and the conduction band but these are acceptor levels which can trap electrons promoted by an energy ΔE_p from the filled band (see *Figure 7.8*). Typical values for ΔE_p are given in

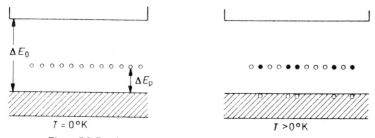

Figure 7.8. Band structure of a p-type impurity semiconductor

Table 7.2. The positive holes so created provide a mechanism for electronic conduction. Thus (p. 115) nonstoichiometric cuprous oxide contains vacant cation sites and an equivalent number of cupric ions which can act as trapping centres for electrons which convert them back to cuprous ions. Again a dynamic equilibrium exists and the conductivity, which depends on the number of defects, is closely related to the pressure.

We can now see an elegant way of deciding whether a given compound is metal excess or metal deficit by following the changes of electrical conductivity with pressure at constant temperature. As shown on p. 117 an increase in the pressure of oxygen above zinc oxide decreases the number of defects (impurity centres) and hence the number of sites potentially able to donate electrons into the conduction band; the conductivity, κ, will therefore decrease with rise in pressure. With metal deficit semiconductors the reverse is true; an increase in the pressure creates more defects (divalent cation trapping centres) and hence the conductivity will rise (p. 120). In this way because of the great sensitivity of electrical measurements, conductivity studies can reveal minute deviations from stoichiometry which are quite undetectable by chemical analysis and can also determine in which direction the deviation is occurring. In favourable cases deviations from ideal stoichiometry as small as 1 part in 10^{10} can be detected, though few substances have ever been obtained as pure as this.

A more detailed analysis of the pressure dependence of electronic semiconductivity sometimes indicates that the impurity centres are not distributed randomly throughout the lattice but interact with other defects to form pairs or clusters. As an illustration we can consider the case of nickel oxide. Increase in oxygen pressure above that appropriate to the stoichiometric compound causes the oxidation of some of the cations and the creation of half this number of vacant cation sites:

$$4Ni_l^{2+} + O_2(g) \rightleftharpoons 4Ni_l^{3+} + 2\square_+ + 2O_l^{2-}$$

Remembering that the concentrations of Ni^{2+} and O^{2-} on normal lattice sites are virtually constant for small deviations from stoichiometry we can write the equilibrium constant for the reaction as

$$K = \frac{[Ni^{3+}]^4\,[\square_+]^2}{p(O_2)}$$

From the stoichiometry of the reaction (electroneutrality):

$$[\square_+] = \tfrac{1}{2}[Ni^{3+}]$$

Hence

$$K = \frac{[Ni^{3+}]^6}{4p(O_2)}$$

and, as the conductivity κ is proportional to $[Ni^{3+}]$

$$\kappa = K'p^{\frac{1}{6}}(O_2)$$

Experimentally, at temperatures high enough for thermodynamic equilibrium to be established, the conductivity was found to vary as $p^{\frac{1}{6}}(O_2)$ as required in the equation.[1]

The pressure dependence of the conductivity of cuprous oxide can be analysed similarly. The equation for the formation of defects is

$$4Cu_l^+ + O_2(g) \rightleftharpoons 4Cu_l^{2+} + 4\square_+ + 2O_l^{2-}$$

[1] Mitoff, S. P., *J. chem. Phys.*, **35** (1961) 882

Here $[Cu^+]$ and $[O^{2-}]$ are effectively constant and $[Cu^{2+}] =$ $[\square_+]$. Hence the equilibrium constant is

$$K = [Cu^{2+}]^8/p(O_2)$$

and the conductivity, which is proportional to the concentration of cupric ions, should be proportional to $p^{\frac{1}{8}}(O_2)$. Experimentally a $p^{\frac{1}{4}}(O_2)$ dependence is found because of the trapping of cupric ions by the virtual negative charges on the vacant cation sites. As a result of this not all the cupric ions contribute to the trapping of the electrons from the full band and to the formation of conducting positive holes in this band.

In some systems it is inconvenient or impracticable to follow the change of conductivity with ambient pressure of one of the components. In such cases, where the deviations from stoichiometry are too small to determine analytically, two further electrical effects can be used to characterize the type of semiconductor and the direction of stoichiometric imbalance. The first is the Seebeck effect (thermoelectric effect) which depends on the sign of the charges on the current carriers. When two ends of a conductor or semiconductor are held at different temperatures a potential difference (ΔV millivolt) which is proportional to the temperature difference, ΔT, develops across the ends:

$$\Delta V = \pm Q\,\Delta T$$

Q is called the thermoelectric power of the material. For p-type, positive-hole semiconductors the cold junction is positive with respect to the hot junction; for n-type, negative electron semiconductors the cold junction is negative.

The second technique is to use the Hall effect (*Figure 7.9*). When

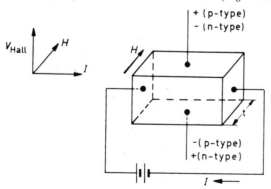

Figure 7.9. Origin of the Hall effect—see text

167

a current, I, is passed through a specimen and a magnetic field, H, is applied at right angles to the direction of current flow, a transverse voltage develops, the sign of which depends on the sign of the current carriers. The magnitude of the voltage V is proportional to both the current and the magnetic field and is inversely proportional to the thickness, t, in the direction of the magnetic field:

$$V = \pm \frac{10^{-8}RIH}{t}$$

The proportionality constant R is called the Hall coefficient and when I is in amps, H in gauss, V in volts, and t in cm then R is in $cm^3 \cdot coulomb^{-1}$. The Hall voltage arises because the magnetic field causes the current carriers to travel in curved paths, resulting in a tendency for them to concentrate on one side of the specimen; this induces a Hall voltage to counteract this transverse flow of current. Thus, applying the conventional rules for the interaction of electric current and magnetic fields: for n-type semiconductors, electrons flow from right to left in the specimen (*Figure 7.9*) and the magnetic field tends to move them up (counterclockwise)—the top of the specimen therefore develops a negative potential to oppose this motion; for p-type semiconductors, positive holes move from left to right and again move to the top of the specimen which therefore develops a positive potential. In this way the sign of the Hall coefficient, R, differentiates n-type from p-type semiconductors and hence metal-excess from metal-deficit nonstoichiometric compounds. Further, $R = \pm 1/(ne)$ where n is the number of current carriers of charge $+e$ (positive holes) or $-e$ (electrons). Since the conductivity $\kappa = nev$, the product of the Hall constant and the conductivity gives the mobility of the current carriers. The last two columns of *Table 7.2* list some typical values. The highest known carrier mobility is 80,000 $cm \cdot sec^{-1}/V \cdot cm^{-1}$ for indium antimonide and mobilities as low as 1–10 $cm \cdot sec^{-1}/V \cdot cm^{-1}$ have been recorded. Electron mobilities, v_n, in a compound are usually greater than positive hole mobilities, v_p, but this is not necessarily so and the reverse is true for boron, black phosphorus, and the compounds Mg_3Sb, $CdSb$, and Sb_2S_3.

As a further illustration of how Hall effect measurements can be used to study nonstoichiometry we can consider the analysis of results on a typical semiconductor such as lead sulphide. *Figure 7.10* shows the concentrations of free electrons and positive holes as determined at room temperature by Hall effect measurements on single crystals of lead sulphide which have been annealed under controlled sulphur vapour pressures at 727° and 950°C. As expected (p. 120) n-type conduction occurs at low pressures and p-type conduction at high pressures with a sharp transition in between. At points sufficiently removed from the transition the slope of the lines shows that the carrier concentration is proportional to $p^{\pm\frac{1}{4}}(S_2)$ as predicted from the equations:

$$Pb_i^{2+} + \tfrac{1}{2}S_2(g) \rightleftharpoons Pb_i^{4+} + \square_+ + S_i^{2-}$$
$$Pb_i^{2+} + S_i^{2-} \rightleftharpoons Pb_i^0 + \square_- + \tfrac{1}{2}S_2(g)$$

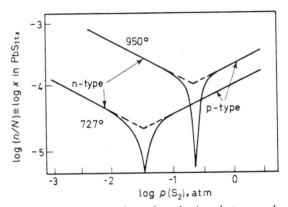

Figure 7.10. Concentrations of conduction electrons and positive holes in lead sulphide at room temperature after annealing under various pressures of sulphur vapour at 727° and 950°C. As the donor and acceptor levels are fully ionized their concentration also represents the deviation from stoichiometry

(Data after J. Bloem, *Philips Res. Rep.* 11 (1956) 273)

The intrinsic energy gap is 8·1 kcal/mole at room temperature and 16 kcal/mole at 800°. The ionization energies of the single vacancies acting as electron donors and acceptors are very small ($E_n \simeq E_p \simeq$ 0·2 kcal/mole) so that all donors and acceptors are ionized at room temperature and the carrier concentration is equal to twice the number of supernumerary lead or sulphur atoms. Extrapolation of the linear limbs therefore defines the point of precise stoichiometry, and the pressure at which the compound $PbS_{1.000}$ is stable is found to vary from $3\cdot2 \times 10^{-2}$ atm (24 mm) at 727° to 2×10^{-1} atm (150 mm) at 950°C. Deviations from stoichiometry in $PbS_{1.000 \pm x}$ are in the range $x \simeq 10^{-3} - 10^{-5}$. For specimens equilibrated at 1 atm $x = 5\cdot3 \times 10^{-5}$ at 530° and $2\cdot1 \times 10^{-3}$ at 975°C. Many more examples of such behaviour, together with a detailed analysis of results, will be found in the references[5, 6] at the end of this chapter.

7.1.6. *Visible and Ultraviolet Absorption Spectra*

Details of the energy band structure and impurity levels of non-stoichiometric solids has come from electrical and magnetic measurements and also from direct observation of transitions between the various energy levels by means of optical absorption spectroscopy. Spectroscopic techniques can also detect transitions between various discrete impurity levels which do not involve the conduction band or the valence band and which therefore can not be detected by electrical conductivity. A vast amount of information has been obtained in this way to supplement and extend the data discussed in the preceding section. Much of the work has been on alkali halide crystals with small deviations from stoichiometry and some of the more important conclusions are now outlined.

When alkali halide crystals are heated in the presence of alkali metal or halogen vapours the crystals take up a stoichiometric excess of one of the components and become highly coloured. For example, sodium chloride when heated in sodium vapour and then rapidly cooled becomes orange-yellow or brown and potassium chloride when treated similarly with potassium vapour becomes violet or magenta. The excess alkali atoms from the vapour ionize at the surface and diffuse into the crystal where they occupy normal lattice sites. An equal number of anion vacancies are created and each vacancy behaves as a positive charge which can trap the electron freed by the ionization of the alkali metal atom. An electron bound to an anion vacancy (i.e. a neutral anion vacancy) is called an F-centre (German *Farbzentre*) because it is the source of the optical absorption giving rise to the colour. It is a particular example of a large number of different types of defects and defect clusters which are collectively known as colour-centres.

The evidence on which this model is based is as follows:

(*a*) the intensity of the band is proportional to the stoichiometric excess of metal, and hence also to the number of anion vacancies;

(*b*) the absorption is characteristic of the crystal and not of the metal vapour: thus potassium chloride develops the same F-band whether it is heated in potassium or sodium vapour and also when it is irradiated by X-rays or other ionizing radiations known to produce free electrons which are then trapped by chloride ion vacancies;

170

(c) the coloured crystals are less dense than the parent stoichiometric crystal, indicating that the predominant lattice defects are anion vacancies, rather than interstitial cations;

(d) paramagnetic susceptibility measurements, which have been confirmed, refined, and extended by electron-spin resonance measurements, establish that an F-centre has a spin contribution corresponding to that of a relatively free electron;

(e) F-centre absorption excites the trapped electron into the conduction band or into energy levels below the conduction band of the crystal; the width of the absorption band is due to the lattice vibrations of the ions.

Typical data for the alkali metal chlorides is given in *Table 7.3*. It can be seen that with increasing atomic number of the metal (decrease in lattice energy) the colour moves to longer wavelengths (lower energy).

Table 7.3
Absorption characteristics of F-centres in alkali metal chlorides at room temperature

Compound	LiCl	NaCl	KCl	RbCl	CsCl
Colour	yellow	orange	violet	blue	blue
λ_{max} mμ	385	465	563	624	603
ΔE_F kcal/mole	74·3	61·5	50·7	45·7	47·5

Many other types of colour centre have been detected by treating alkali halide crystals under a variety of conditions. Some are stable at room temperature while others are transient even at very low temperatures. Their study has given considerable insight into the formation, concentration, and stability of various defects and defect clusters. Some of the more important colour centres are listed in *Table 7.4*. Their nomenclature has developed somewhat haphazardly and tends to be arbitrary, confused, and sometimes inconsistent. A pictorial representation of some of these defects is given in *Figure 7.11*. It is important to distinguish clearly between the colour centres (defects) themselves, and the optical absorptions to which they give rise; the latter are energy transitions between the colour centre in its ground state and one of its excited states. Thus a given colour centre may give rise to more than one optical transition. For example, the trapped electron in an F-centre can be excited to the conduction band or to exciton levels (F-band and K-band) or the F-centre can trap an additional electron from the valence band of the crystal (β-band) and become converted to an

171

Table 7.4

Description of some colour centres (see also *Figure 7.11* and text)

Colour centre	Defect cluster*	Description
α	$\square_-$	vacant anion site with virtual positive charge
F	$(\square_- + e^-)$	neutral anion vacancy
F'	$(\square_- + 2e^-)$	vacant anion site with negative charge
R_1	$(2\square_- + e^-)$	two adjacent neutral anion vacancies minus one electron
R_2	$(2\square_- + 2e^-)$	two adjacent neutral anion vacancies
M	$(2\square_- + \square_+ + e^-)$	neutral association of two anion vacancies and one cation vacancy
$V_M V_X$	$(\square_+ + \square_-)$	cation and anion vacancy pair
V_1	$(\square_+ + p^+)$	neutral cation vacancy
V_2	$(2\square_+ + 2p^+)$	two adjacent neutral cation vacancies
V_3	$(2\square_+ + p^+)$	two adjacent neutral cation vacancies minus one positive hole

* $\square_-$ represents a vacant anion site with its associated virtual positive charge

$\square_+$ represents a vacant cation site with its associated virtual negative charge

e^- represents a bound electron

p^+ represents a bound positive hole

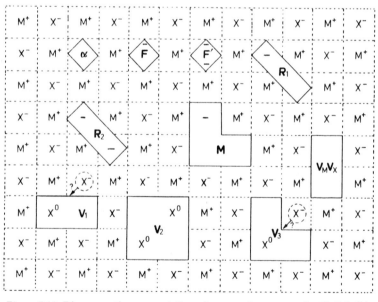

Figure 7.11. Diagrammatic representation of some colour centres in alkali halide crystals (see also *Table 7.4*)

F'-centre, leaving a positive hole in the valence band. This is represented schematically in *Figure 7.12*.

The techniques for generating the various colour centres, the experimental methods for investigating them, and the theoretical analysis of the results obtained have recently been reviewed in considerable detail (e.g. in references 5, 7, 8, and 9 at the end of the chapter) and will not be repeated here. It will be sufficient to allude

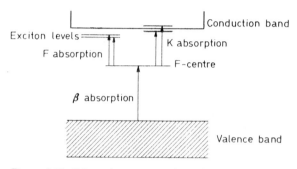

Figure 7.12. Schematic representation of various possible absorption processes showing electronic transitions to or from an F-centre

briefly to the results on a single compound, potassium chloride. When potassium chloride is irradiated with X-rays or equilibrated at high temperatures with an excess of potassium and then cooled, F-centres are generated as indicated above. When the coloured crystals are irradiated at low temperatures with light in the F-band frequency range they become photoconducting due to the promotion of some of the trapped electrons into the conduction band. This converts the F-centres into simple anion vacancies (with virtual positive charges) and subsequently the conduction electrons can be trapped by other F-centres, thus transforming them into F'-centres. As a consequence of these changes, irradiation with F-band light diminishes the intensity of the F- and β-absorption bands and simultaneously generates new absorptions corresponding to an F'-band (promotion of an electron from the newly formed F'-centre) and an α-band (trapping of an electron from the valence band by the newly formed simple vacant anion site). The changes in absorption are depicted schematically in *Figure 7.13*. On warming to a temperature just sufficient to decompose the F'-centres the F'- and α-bands disappear and the F- and β-bands are regenerated to their original intensity:

$$F' + \alpha \underset{\substack{\text{low temp.}\\\text{irradiation}}}{\overset{\text{warm}}{\rightleftharpoons}} 2F$$

i.e. $\qquad (\square_- + 2e^-) + (\square_-) \rightleftharpoons 2(\square_- + e^-)$

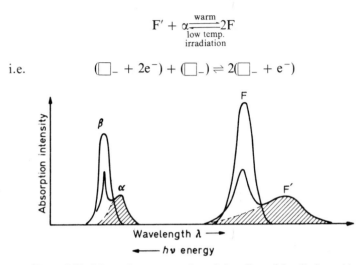

Figure 7.13. Schematic representation of the effect of irradiation with F-band light; the intensity of the F and β-bands diminish and two new bands corresponding to F' and α appear

When alkali halide crystals are equilibrated with halogen vapou at high temperatures or irradiated by X-rays at liquid nitrogen temperature V-bands appear, associated with cation vacancies. Irradiation of the crystals with F-band light or warming the crystals to $-150°$ bleaches the V_1-band, slightly increases the intensity of the V_2-band and excites photoconduction. This is consistent with the view that the V_1-centre is a cation vacancy and trapped positive hole (neutral cation vacancy). The hole can escape from the trap by acquiring a small amount of thermal energy which bleaches the V-band and the hole can annihilate an electron trapped at an F-centre, thus simultaneously bleaching the F-band. Other models have also been proposed involving various combinations of cation vacancies and molecular halogen species X_2, X_2^- etc.; thus for V_1 and V_3 in *Figure 7.11* a slight diagonal motion of the X^- ion adjacent to the cation vacancy in the direction of the neutral halogen atom could lead to the formation of X_2^- and a similar interaction of the unpaired spins in V_2 might lead to the molecular species X_2, perhaps in an excited state. Such problems are currently being studied by electron spin resonance techniques. Likewise irradiation of a crystal at liquid helium temperatures generates the unstable H-band which may be due to X_2^- occupying a normal X^- lattice site. In this way, by various combinations of irradiation followed by thermal or optical bleaching the general picture of colour centres as aggregates of specific lattice defects of varying charge has emerged. Actual deviations from stoichiometry depend on the conditions of preparation and are normally in the range 10^{-3}–10^{-6}. For potassium chloride the energies and wavelengths of typical transitions are as follows:

Band	β	α	K	F	F′	R_1	R_2	M	V_1	V_2	H_1
ΔE (kcal/mole)	168	160	65	51	41	43	39	36	80	118	83
λ_{max} (mμ)	170	180	440	550	700	680	740	800	360	240	245

7.2. Summary of Results on Nonstoichiometric Compounds

Historically, the transition-element oxides have attracted more attention than probably any other systems and we have already discussed the results obtained on the various oxides of titanium (pp. 131, 143), vanadium (p. 131), iron (pp. 135, 152), cobalt (p. 133), nickel (p. 166), copper (p. 166), zinc (pp. 116, 164), cadmium (p. 114), cerium (p. 138), praseodymium (p. 138), molybdenum (p. 142), tungsten (p. 142) and uranium (pp. 135, 150). Further work on these and on oxides of other transition elements such as Mn, Cr, Zr, Hf, Nb and Ta will be found in references 1, 10 and 11 at the end of the chapter. Main-group oxides, such as those of tin and lead (p. 153) have also been studied. The work on transition-element chalcogenides is currently attracting increasing attention and certain results have already been alluded to, e.g. the sulphide of titanium (p. 153), chromium (p. 140), iron (p. 139), cobalt (p. 122), copper (p. 122), and lead (p. 168); see also references 1, 10 and 11. Metal hydrides form another broad class of nonstoichiometric compounds (p. 158 and references 1 and 11), and the alkali metal halides have been treated in the preceding section. The general principles set out in Chapter 6 indicate that nonstoichiometry is expected in two further classes of binary compound:

(a) intermetallic compounds and related systems such as metal borides, carbides, silicides, phosphides etc. (see reference 17 for a recent review of these latter systems);

(b) tetrahedral structures comprising III–V and II–VI compounds (see reference 3).

Little point would be served in enumerating further examples of nonstoichiometry within these classes.

When ternary compounds are considered many new possibilities arise and the case of isomorphous substitution in the spinel system has already been discussed from several points of view. Less work has been done on ternary systems in general though specific structure-types have been the subject of intensive study. One such system which involves the ReO_3 and perovskite structures, leads to the formation of the tungsten bronzes and related substances. The structural relations and main physical properties of these bronzes will therefore be briefly reviewed.

The open, cubic structure of ReO_3 has been illustrated on p. 141. If the cube centre is occupied by a cation of appropriate charge and size the perovskite structure ABO_3 is obtained, as shown in *Figure 7.14*. The structure is one of the most prevalent types for ternary

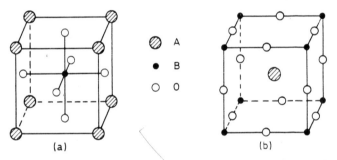

Figure 7.14. (a) Perovskite structure ABO_3. (b) The same structure with the unit cell origin shifted by $\frac{1}{2}\frac{1}{2}\frac{1}{2}$ to show the close relationship of the perovskite structure to the ReO_3 structure (*Figure 6.7*)

oxides and also includes some ternary halides such as $KMgF_3$, $RbCaF_3$. With oxides the sum of the cationic charges must be $+6$ and this can be obtained by having a 1,5, a 2,4, or a 3,3 combination, or by various more complex substitutional patterns. The geometry of the unit cell dictates that the radius criterion is

$$(r_A + r_O) \simeq (\sqrt{2})(r_B + r_O)$$

The perovskite structure, or slight distortions of it, is adopted by some 300 ternary oxides and many of these have extremely interesting dielectric and magnetic properties, e.g. $BaTiO_3$ is ferroelectric,

$PbZrO_3$ is antiferroelectric, $LaCo_{0.2}Mn_{0.8}O_3$ is ferromagnetic and $LaFeO_3$ is antiferromagnetic.

Nonstoichiometry arises when compounds which adopt the ReO_3 structure (or some closely related distortion of it) take up variable amounts of a second metal at the A site; the classic examples are the tungsten bronzes M_xWO_3 where M is an alkali metal, copper, silver, thallium, or lead. Bronzes having a similar cubic cage structure are known for M_xBO_3 where B is Nb, Ta and Ti. The sodium tungsten bronzes can be considered as typical of the group. They are formed (a) by a solid-phase reaction between sodium tungstate, tungsten and tungstic oxide, (b) the reduction of sodium tungstate and tungstic oxide with hydrogen, or (c) the vapour phase reduction of tungstic oxide by sodium:

$$(a)\ \frac{x}{2}Na_2WO_4 + \frac{3-2x}{3}WO_3 + \frac{x}{6}W = Na_xWO_3$$

$$(b)\ \frac{x}{2}Na_2WO_4 + \left(1 - \frac{x}{2}\right)WO_3 + \frac{x}{2}H_2 = Na_xWO_3 + \frac{x}{2}H_2O$$

$$(c)\ WO_3 + xNa = Na_xWO_3$$

The properties of the tungsten bronzes depend on the sodium content; they are blue when $x \sim 0.4$, purple-red when $x \sim 0.6$ and yellow with a metallic lustre when $x \sim 0.8$. The energy band structure of WO_3 is such that the vacant $5d_\varepsilon$ orbitals (d_{xy}, d_{yz}, d_{zx}) overlap to form an empty conduction band. The added sodium atoms constitute donor impurity sites about 0.9 kcal/mole below this band so that, at room temperature and above, the supernumerary electrons are almost entirely in the conduction band whence the metallic properties of the crystals. The following evidence is consistent with this picture:

(a) the metallic conductivity decreases linearly with temperature;

(b) the Hall effect shows that the free electron concentration equals the sodium atom concentration; at lower temperatures the activation energy for promotion from the donor level to the conduction band is found to be 0.9 kcal/mole.

(c) the weak paramagnetism of the bronzes is temperature independent, implying that the electrons are not localized on specific tungsten atoms (W^{5+}); the conductivity is therefore not due to an electron-hopping process as in Fe_3O_4;

(d) there is no appreciable Knight shift (strong paramagnetic positive shift) of the nuclear magnetic resonance signal for ^{23}Na

indicating that the density of the conduction electrons at the sodium nuclei is essentially zero;

(e) the higher the sodium content, the greater the number of $5d_\varepsilon$ conduction band levels which are occupied, hence the greater the energy required to promote electrons from the donor levels to the top of the Fermi surface in the conduction band; this is reflected in the colour changes of the bronzes, i.e. the shift of the optical absorption band to progressively increasing energies (shorter wavelengths) as the sodium content is increased.

Other nonstoichiometric bronzes with different crystal structures are known. Sodium titanium bronze, Na_xTiO_2 ($0.20 < x < 0.25$), can be prepared by heating a mixture of $Na_2Ti_3O_7$, TiO_2 and Ti. It shows a relatively high, metallic-type conductivity, a low, temperature-independent paramagnetic susceptibility and an electronic absorption spectrum consistent with the delocalized conduction-electron model involving overlap of the Ti $3d_\varepsilon$ orbitals.[1] The sodium vanadium bronzes $Na_xV_2O_5$ ($0.16 < x < 0.33$) are somewhat different: here the electron from the sodium is transferred to a V^{5+} to form a localized V^{4+} centre from which electron-excitation to the host conduction band can occur.[2] Hall-effect measurements indicate that electrons are the current carriers but that not all impurity centres are ionized at the lower temperatures; consistent with this the vanadium bronzes show a pronounced paramagnetic susceptibility from the localized unpaired electrons. However, electron spin resonance, nuclear magnetic resonance and the electrical measurements rule out a hopping mechanism for the conduction and point to thermal promotion into a conduction band. Other vanadium bronzes $M_xV_2O_5$ (in which M is an alkali metal, copper, or silver and $x \sim 0.3$) behave similarly.

Semiconducting properties in perovskite phases can also be induced by isomorphous substitution. For example if, in barium titanate $BaTiO_3$, some of the barium ions (Ba^{2+} 1.35 Å) are replaced by lanthanum ions (La^{3+} 1.15 Å) then the same number of Ti^{4+} ions must be reduced to Ti^{3+} to preserve charge-balance:

$$La_x^{3+}Ba_{(1-x)}^{2+}Ti_{(1-x)}^{4+}O_3.$$

The material becomes an n-type semiconductor by virtue of the presence of the Ti^{3+} ions on Ti^{4+} sites. Mixed-valence perovskites can also lead to ferromagnetic exchange, e.g.

$$La_x^{3+}Sr_{(1-x)}^{2+}[Mn_x^{3+}Mn_{(1-x)}^{4+}]O_3.$$

[1] Reid, A. F. and Sienko, M. J., *Inorg. Chem.*, **6** (1967) 321

[2] Sienko, M. J. and Sohn, J. B., *J. chem. Phys.* **44** (1966) 1369

When $x = 1$ we have $LaMn^{3+}O_3$, when $x = 0$ we have $SrMn^{4+}O_3$ and for $0 < x < 1$ the compound has a high electrical conductivity. When $0.6 < x < 0.8$ the conductivity is metallic and the compound is ferromagnetic with a moment approaching that for complete alignment of all the manganese spins; this is confirmed by neutron diffraction.

7.3. Some Applications of Nonstoichiometric Compounds

One of the main stimuli to research in defect ionic solids has been the dependence of certain important physical properties on minute deviations from stoichiometry. Semiconduction, photoconduction, fluorescence, and thermoelectricity have been employed in such industrial products as sensitive thermistor thermometers, photoelectric cells, rectifiers, transistors, phosphors, luminescent materials and computer components. Each of these devices in turn has found innumerable applications. Inorganic pigments whose colour is a function of the nature and concentration of the defects are extensively used in the paint industry. In photography the problems of sensitivity, formation of the latent image and the process of its development are all associated with defect phenomena.

In addition, the properties of electrode surfaces and the performance of electric batteries depend markedly on the essential presence of nonstoichiometric defects. Heterogeneous catalysis involving solid surfaces is another area where lattice defects play a vital role and, indeed, the fact that solid-state reactions can proceed at all requires the presence of vacancies or interstitials to enable the reacting species to move through the crystal; the diffusion of these species implies concentration gradients and hence nonstoichiometry within at least one of the reacting phases. The corrosion and tarnishing of solids are related examples; not only do they depend on the existence of defects but they can often be controlled by counter-defects, as in the formation of passive oxide films or the addition of impurities to inhibit the rate of corrosion. Phase transformations, crystal growth from the melt or solution, and the dissolution or etching of solids are also all intimately dependent on the existence of lattice defects though these are not necessarily nonstoichiometric. Each of these topics is a monograph in itself and numerous treatises, reviews, and semi-technical accounts have appeared on each individual application. Reference is made to some of these at the end of the chapter.

The implications of nonstoichiometry in analytical chemistry are obvious. Precise gravimetric analysis depends on the preparation of accurately stoichiometric compounds and considerable attention must frequently be paid to the conditions necessary to eliminate stoichiometric imbalance or the formation of solid solutions of impurities. The compounds typically used in such analytical work are chosen for their minimal susceptibility to these effects. A simple numerical illustration indicates the possible magnitude of the effect: cuprous iodide, when heated in an atmosphere of iodine vapour can deviate as far as the composition $CuI_{1.0045}$; the atomic weight of iodine calculated from such a crystal would be 127·5 instead of 126·9.

References for Further Reading

1. 'Nonstoichiometric Compounds', *Adv. Chem. Ser.*, **39**, 1963
2. Bacon, G. E., 'Applications of Neutron Diffraction in Chemistry' *The International Encyclopedia of Physical Chemistry and Chemical Physics*, Pergamon Press, Oxford, 1963
3. Hannay, N. B. (Ed.), *Semiconductors*, Reinhold, New York, 1959
4. Shockley, W. S., *Electrons, Holes, and Semiconductors*, Van Nostrand, New York, 1950
5. Kröger, F. A., *The Chemistry of Imperfect Crystals*, North-Holland, Amsterdam, 1964
6. Putley, E. H., *The Hall Effect and Related Phenomena*, Butterworths, London, 1960
7. Mott, N. F. and Gurney, R. W., *Electronic Processes in Ionic Crystals*, Oxford University Press, 1950
8. Garner, W. E. (Ed.), *Chemistry of the Solid State*, Butterworths, London, 1955
9. Markham, J. J., 'F-Centres in Alkali Halides', *Solid St. Phys.* Suppl. 8, Academic Press, New York, 1966
10. Wadsley, A. D., 'Inorganic Nonstoichiometric Compounds', Chapt. 3 in Mandelcorn, L. (Ed.), *Nonstoichiometric Compounds*, Academic Press, New York, 1964
11. Libowitz, G. G., 'Nonstoichiometry in Chemical Compounds', *Prog. Solid St. Chem.*, **2** (1964) 216–264
12. Kröger, F. A. and Vink, H. J., 'Relations between Concentrations of Imperfections in Crystalline Solids', *Solid St. Phys.*, **3** (1956) 307–435
13. Hauffe, K., *Reaktionen in und an Festen Stoffen*, Springer-Verlag, Berlin, 1955
14. Gray, T. J., Detwiler, D. P., Rase, D. E., Lawrence, W. G., West, R. R. and Jennings, T. J., *The Defect Solid State*, Interscience, New York, 1957

REFERENCES

15. Rees, A. L. G., 'Significance of Solid State Defects in Chemical Science and Technology', *Aust. J. Sci.,* **26** (1964) 239–46
16. Tompkins, F. C., 'Imperfections and Chemical Reactivity', *Pure appl. Chem.,* **5** (1962) 501–512
17. Aronsson, B., Rundqvist, S. and Lundstrom, T., *Borides, Silicides and Phosphides,* Methuen, London, 1965

N

APPENDIX

Ionization Potentials of the Elements

$1 \text{ kcal} = 4 \cdot 1833 \text{ kJ} = 4 \cdot 3359 \text{ eV}$

Atomic number	Element	Ionization potential (kcal/g. atom)						
		1st	2nd	3rd	4th	5th	6th	7th
1	H	313·6						
2	He	566·8	1254·5					
3	Li	124·3	1743·8	2822·5				
4	Be	214·9	419·9	3548·9	5020			
5	B	191·3	580·0	874·4	5798	7845		
6	C	259·6	562·2	1103·6	1487	9039	11294	
7	N	335·3	682·8	1093·7	1786	2256	12727	1537
8	O	313·8	810·6	1266·8	1785	2626	3185	1704
9	F	401·7	806·6	1444·7	2012	2633	3623	462
10	Ne	497·2	947·1	1475·8	2241	2915	3641	
11	Na	118·4	1090·5	1652·2	2280	3196	3999	480
12	Mg	176·3	346·6	1847·6	2521	3256	4310	519
13	Al	138·0	434·0	655·8	2583	3547	4391	557
14	Si	187·9	376·8	771·6	1041	3844	4730	476
15	P	243·3	453·1	695·5	1184	1499	5082	607
16	S	238·9	539·6	807·1	1091	1672	2030	648
17	Cl	300·0	548·8	920·0	1234	1563	2230	263
18	Ar	363·4	636·9	943·1	1379	1730	2105	285
19	K	100·0	733·5	1060·6	1404		2299	272
20	Ca	140·9	273·7	1180·9	1545	1946		295
21	Sc	151·3	295·2	570·7	1704	2121	2562	318
22	Ti	157·5	312·9	648·9	997	2301	2767	324
23	V	155·4	337·8	684·9	1107	1504	2972	348
24	Cr	156·0	380·2	715	1162	1685	2090	371
25	Mn	171·4	360·6	738	1200	1750	2260	274
26	Fe	182·2	373·1	757·0	1315	1800	2350	295
27	Co	181·3	393·2	772·1	1220	1925	2445	304
28	Ni	176·0	418·5	810·6	1290	1800	2540	314
29	Cu	178·1	467·9	680·3	1358	1890	2445	323
30	Zn	216·6	414·2	922·3	1430	1980	2580	328
31	Ga	138·4	473·0	705·6	1471			

ıization Potentials—*continued*

tomic umber	Element	Ionization potential (kcal/g. atom)						
		1st	2nd	3rd	4th	5th	6th	7th
32	Ge	181·7	367·3	785·7	1049	2145		
33	As	226·2	465·8	645·7	1151	1441		
34	Se	224·8	495·8	781·7	985	1678	1877	
35	Br	273·0	498·1	592·6	1153			
36	Kr	322·8	566·4	848·6	1568			
37	Rb	96·3	634·2	1084	1845			
38	Sr	131·2	254·4					
39	Y	147·1	282·0	470·4				
40	Zr	157·6	297·9	553·4	779	1910	2280	2720
41	Nb	158·7	320·2	558·1	882	1140	2380	2880
42	Mo	164·4	352·1	622	933	1290	1660	2880
43	Tc	166·7	342·9	668	991	1360	1750	2165
44	Ru	169·8	382·6	659	1070	1450	1870	2310
45	Rh	172·1	367·1	714	1050	1545	1960	2420
46	Pd	192·1	447·8	770	1125	1520	2070	2530
47	Ag	174·7	495·3	827·9	1198	1610	2050	2670
48	Cd	207·3	389·7	876·3				
49	In	133·4	434·2	643·4	1333			
50	Sn	169·1	337·4	703·3	909	1859		
51	Sb	199·2	438·1	569·6	1015	1280		
52	Te	207·7	495·8	703·3	869	1384	1660	
53	I	240·7	438·1					
54	Xe	279·7	489·1	737·9	1061	1753		
55	Cs	89·3	578·8	807	1176	1337		
56	Ba	120·1	230·6					
57	La	129·4	263·6	470·4				
58	Ce	159	341·3					
59	Pr	133						
60	Nd	145·3						
61	Pm	—						
62	Sm	129	258					
63	Eu	130·8	259					
64	Gd	142·0	276					
65	Tb	155						
66	Dy	157						
67	Ho	—						
68	Er	140						

Ionization Potentials—*continued*

Atomic number	Element	Ionization potential (kcal/g. atom)						
		1st	2nd	3rd	4th	5th	6th	7t▌
69	Tm	141						
70	Yb	143	279					
71	Lu	142	339					
72	Hf	127	343	485	715			
73	Ta	178	—	515	763	1040		
74	W	184	323	555	815	1105	1405	
75	Re	182	302	600	868	1175	1475	182
76	Os	200	346	576	920	1240	1570	191
77	Ir	210	370	622	900	1310	1660	203
78	Pt	208	428·0	656	946	1270	1730	212
79	Au	212·6	472·7	692	1002	1340	1680	221
80	Hg	240·5	432·4	791	1660	1890		
81	Tl	140·8	470·9	685	1165			
82	Pb	171·0	346·0	736	971	1600		
83	Bi	168·0	445·0	586	1040	1284		
84	Po	194						
85	At	212						
86	Rn	247·9						
87	Fr	91·8						
88	Ra	121·7	233·8					
89	Ac	158		678				
90	Th	160						
91	Pa	—						
92	U	92						

INDEX

Ahrens, L. H., 33, 36
Alkali-metal halides (*see* CsCl, KCl, NaCl, etc.)
Alloys (*see* Intermetallic compounds)
α-centres, 172–175
Aluminium mono- and dichlorides, disproportionation of, 23
Aluminium oxide, Madelung constant of, 19
Ammonium trifluorotrioxomolybdate, 105, 106
Analytical chemistry, implications of nonstoichiometry in, 179, 180
Anatase, Madelung constant of, 19
Anderson, J. S., 124, 147, 153, 156
Andersson, S., 131
Angles, law of constant interfacial, 1
Antiferroelectric $PbZrO_3$, 177
Antiferromagnetic $LaFeO_3$, 177
Applications of nonstoichiometric compounds, 179, 180
Ariya, S. M., 134, 135
Aronson, S., 150
Aronsson, B., 181
Atomic numbers of the elements, 182–184
Avogadro's number and lattice defects, 78

Bacon, G. E., 180
Band theory, 161–165 (*see also* Conduction bands)
Barlow, W., 2
Bartlett, N., 24
Bartolinus, Erasmus, 1
Bauminger, R., 102
Belle, J., 150
Bénard, J., 154
Berthollet–Proust controversy, 5, 111
β-band, 171, 173–175
β-brass, nonstoichiometry in, 112
order-disorder in, 88–90
structure, 50
Bevan, D. J. M., 109, 138
Bijvoet, J. M., 8
Blasse, G., 109
Born–Haber cycle, 4, 20–27

Born, M., 18, 28, 44
Born repulsion of ions, 15, 29, 42
Bradley, A. J., 109
Bragg, (W. H. and) W. L., 4, 8, 38
Bravais lattices, 2, 3
Breckenridge, R. G., 79
Bronzes, 133, 176–178
titanium, 178
tungsten, 133, 176–178
vanadium, 178

C-type rare-earth oxide structure, 137
Cadmium chloride, Madelung constant of, 19
structure, 47, 58, 59
relation to CdI_2 structure, 58
Cadmium iodide, Madelung constant of, 19
structure, 47, 56–58
relation to $CdCl_2$ structure, 58
relation to NiAs structure, 57
relation to NiAs structure and nonstoichiometry, 130, 139, 140, 146, 153–155
Caesium chloride, Born–Haber cycle for, 21
Madelung constant of, 19
structure, 48–50
and radius-ratio rules, 43–46
Caesium difluoride, heat of formation of, 23
Calcium carbonate, 1, 4
Calcium chloride, Madelung constant of, 19
Calcium fluoride, activation energy of ionic migration in, 76
defect structures, 107–109, 136, 138, 139, 146, 153, 158, 159
doped with YF_3, density of, 78, 115
energy of defect formation in, 76
Madelung constant of, 19
structure, 4, 54, 55
and radius-ratio rules, 46, 47
Frenkel defects in, 72, 73
relation to ZnS structure, 54, 137
Carbon dioxide and radius-ratio rules, 46

185

189

Marinov, A., 102
Markham, J. J., 180
Maurer, R., 85
Mayer, J. E., 28, 44
Metal hydrides (*see* Hydrides)
Metals (*see* Band theory, Intermetallic compounds, Order–disorder phenomena, etc.)
Microdomains (*see* Submicroheterogeneity)
Miller indices, 2, 7
Mischenko, K. P., 26
Mitoff, S. P., 166
Mitscherlich, E., 6
Mobility of electrons (and positive holes), 163, 168
Mobility of ions (defects), 75, 149
Modified zirconia, 150
Molar heat capacity (*see* Specific heat)
Molybdenum oxides, substoichiometric, 142–145
Morozova, M. P., 134
Morris, D. F. C., 36
Morrish, A. H., 104
Mössbauer spectroscopy, 8
  and lattice defects, 82
Mössbauer spectrum
  Fe_3O_4, 101, 102
  γ-Fe_2O_3, 104
Mott, N. F., 71, 81, 85, 180

N-type semiconductors (*see* Band theory, Semiconductors, etc.)
Native imperfections (*see* Inherent defects)
Néel's theory of ferrimagnetism, 160
Neon chloride, lattice energy of hypothetical, 21, 22
Neutron diffraction, 8, 135, 148, 157–161
Nickel arsenide structure, 48, 52, 53
  relation to CdI_2 structure, 57
  and nonstoichiometry, 130, 139, 140, 146, 153–155
Nickel oxide, nonstoichiometric, dependence of conductivity on pressure, 166
Nickel telluride, wide composition range of, 130
Nicklow, R. M., 77
Nonstoichiometric compounds (*see also* Nonstoichiometry)
  applications of, 179, 180

Nonstoichiometry, 111 ff.
  and analytical chemistry, 179, 180
  and atomic weight determinations, 180
  and electron diffraction, 161
  and ionic conductivity, 148
  and Mössbauer spectroscopy, 148
  and neutron diffraction, 157–160
  and pressure–composition isotherms, 114, 117–120, 125–129, 148–156
  and quasihomogeneous arrays of defects, 131–133
  and semiconductivity, 164–170
  and shear structures, 131, 140–146
  and submicroheterogeneity, 131, 133–136
  and superlattice ordering of defects, 131, 136–140, 146
  concept of, 5
  conditions necessary for, 122, 123, 146
  direction of deviation, 121, 122
  experimental investigation of, 148–175
  factors influencing extent of, 122–130, 146
  gross deviations, 130–140, 146
  influence of d-orbital radial functions on, 133
  in tungsten bronzes, 177–179
  modes of incorporation, 111–114
  summary of results on, 175–179
  range of composition variation, 121–146
  thermodynamics of, 114–121, 148–152
Novikov, G. I., 36
Nuclear magnetic resonance and lattice defects, 82
  and tungsten bronzes, 177
Nuclear resonance fluorescence (*see* Mössbauer spectroscopy)
Nyburg, S. C., 26

Octet theory, 13
Ofer, S., 102
Ono, K., 102
Optical absorption spectra, 8, 149, 170–175
Order–disorder phenomena, 87–92
  and superlattice ordering of defects, 138
  relation to substitutional nonstoichiometry, 112, 113